Popular Mechanics

do-it-yourself encyclopedia

The complete, illustrated home reference guide from the world's most authoritative source for today's how-to-do-it information.

Volume 25

TRANSMISSIONS AND DRIVE LINE

to

WEEKEND SAFETY TIPS

HEARST DIRECT BOOKS

NEW YORK

Acknowledgements

The Popular Mechanics Encyclopedia is published with the consent and cooperation of POPULAR MECHANICS Magazine.

For POPULAR MECHANICS Magazine:

Editor-in-Chief: *Joe Oldham*

Managing Editor: *Bill Hartford*

Special Features Editor: *Sheldon M. Gallager*

Automotive Editor: *Wade A. Hoyt, SAE*

Home and Shop Editor: *Steve Willson*

Electronics Editor: *Stephen A. Booth*

Boating, Outdoors and Travel Editor: *Timothy H. Cole*

Science Editor: *Dennis Eskow*

Popular Mechanics Encyclopedia

Project Director: *Boyd Griffin*

Manufacturing: *Ron Schoenfeld*

Assistant Editors: *Cynthia W. Lockhart Peter McCann, Rosanna Petruccio*

Production Coordinator: *Peter McCann*

The staff of Popular Mechanics Encyclopedia is grateful to the following individuals and organizations:

Editor: *C. Edward Cavert*

Editor Emeritus: *Clifford B. Hicks*

Production: *Layla Productions*

Production Director: *Lori Stein*

Book Design: *The Bentwood Studio*

Art Director: *Jos. Trautwein*

Design Consultant: *Suzanne Bennett & Associates*

Illustrations: *AP Graphics, Evelyne Johnson Associates, Popular Mechanics Magazine, Vantage Art.*

Contributing Writers: Walter E. Burton, *Metal tubing: look what you can make*, page 3109; John Capotosto, *Colonial weather station*, page 3172; Richard F. Dempewolff, *Save yourself from drowning*, page 3183; George Emory, *Boating emergencies*, page 3187; Lee Green and Paul Stenquist, *Inside moves*, page 3179, (Illustrator, Bryce Lee); William Hampton, *Safe cycling secrets*, page 3195; R.S. Hedin, *Thinwall conduit makes rugged masts*, page 3113; Len Hilts, *Upholstery basic course*, page 3115; *Respring and upholstered chair*, page 3123; W. Clyde Lammey, *Banjo barometer*, page 3176; Mike McClintock, *Summer Houses*, page 3143; Doug Newman, *Fell a tree with a two-man saw*, page 3104; Richard V. Nunn, *Wallpaper: selecting it, buying it*, page 3150; V. Lee Oertle, *Be a savvy RV pilot*, page 3192; Leonard E. Sabal, *Vacation home plans*, page 3131; Mort Schultz, *Automatic transmission service*, page 3083; *Differential troubleshooting*, page 3095; Brad Sears, *Cable-operated shifter adjustments*, page 3089; Gerald Zuhlke, *Accurate water barometer*, page 3174.

Picture Credits: Popular Mechanics Encyclopedia is grateful to the following for permission to reprint their photographs: Road Rider—America's first touring motorcycle magazine, page 3195.

ISBN 0-87851-178-4

Library of Congress 85-81760

10 9 8 7 6 5 4 3 2

PRINTED IN THE UNITED STATES OF AMERICA

Although every effort has been made to ensure the accuracy and completeness of the information in this book, Hearst Direct Books makes no guarantees, stated or implied, nor will they be liable in the event of misinterpretation or human error made by the reader, or for any typographical errors that may appear. WORK SAFELY WITH HAND TOOLS. WEAR SAFETY GOGGLES. READ MANUFACTURER'S INSTRUCTIONS AND WARNINGS FOR ALL PRODUCTS.

PIPE FITTINGS

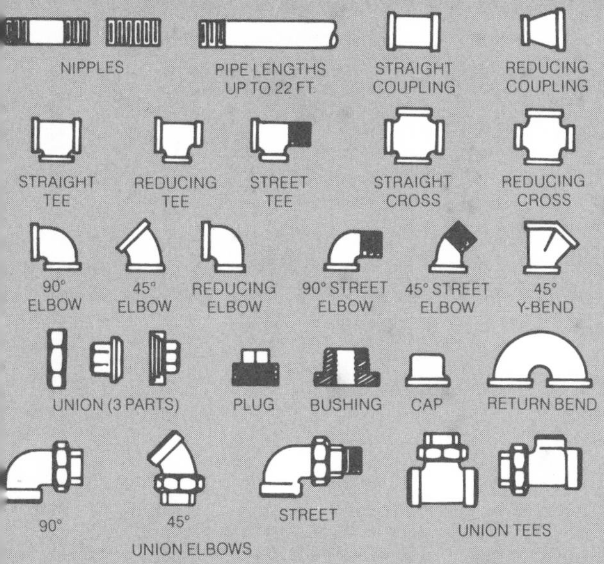

NIPPLES

PIPE LENGTHS UP TO 22 FT.

STRAIGHT COUPLING

REDUCING COUPLING

COUPLING

NUT

CAP

STRAIGHT TEE

REDUCING TEE

STREET TEE

STRAIGHT CROSS

REDUCING CROSS

90° ELBOW

90° ELBOW

90° ELBOW

45° ELBOW

REDUCING ELBOW

90° STREET ELBOW

45° STREET ELBOW

45° Y-BEND

REDUCING TEE

REDUCER

UNION (3 PARTS)

PLUG

BUSHING

CAP

RETURN BEND

90°

45°

STREET

UNION ELBOWS

UNION TEES

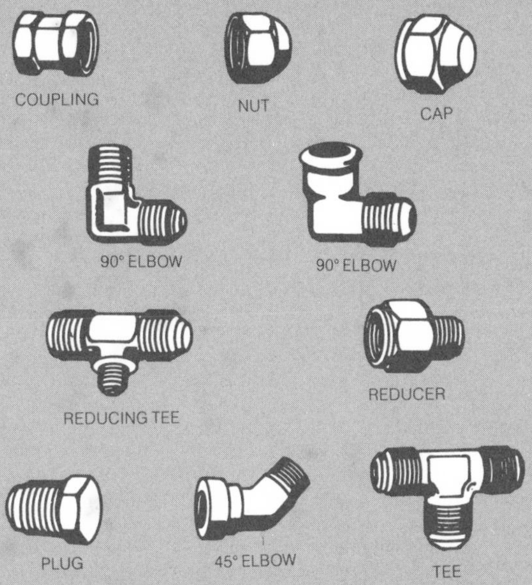

PLUG

45° ELBOW

TEE

MEASURES OF CAPACITY

1 cup = 8 fl oz
2 cups = 1 pint
2 pints = 1 quart
4 quarts = 1 gallon
2 gallons = 1 peck
4 pecks = 1 bushel

STANDARD STEEL PIPE ((All Dimensions in inches)					
Nominal Size	Outside Diameter	Inside Diameter	Nominal Size	Outside Diameter	Inside Diameter
⅛	0.405	0.269	1	1.315	1.049
¼	0.540	0.364	1¼	1.660	1.380
⅜	0.675	0.493	1½	1.900	1.610
½	0.840	0.622	2	2.375	2.067
¾	1.050	0.824	2½	2.875	2.469

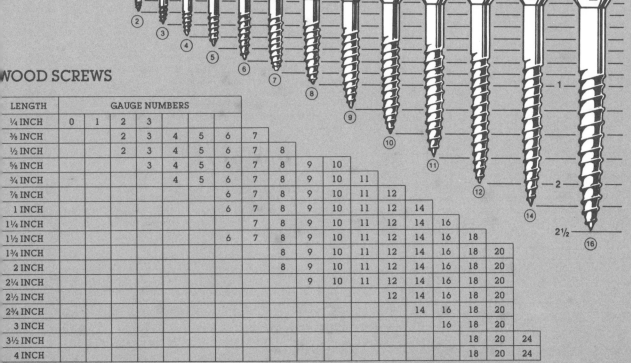

WOOD SCREWS

LENGTH	GAUGE NUMBERS													
¼ INCH	0	1	2	3										
⅜ INCH			2	3	4	5	6	7						
½ INCH			2	3	4	5	6	7	8					
⅝ INCH				3	4	5	6	7	8	9	10			
¾ INCH					4	5	6	7	8	9	10	11		
⅞ INCH							6	7	8	9	10	11	12	
1 INCH							6	7	8	9	10	11	12	14
1¼ INCH								7	8	9	10	11	12	14	16
1½ INCH							6	7	8	9	10	11	12	14	16	18
1¾ INCH									8	9	10	11	12	14	16	18	20
2 INCH									8	9	10	11	12	14	16	18	20
2¼ INCH										9	10	11	12	14	16	18	20
2½ INCH													12	14	16	18	20
2¾ INCH														14	16	18	20
3 INCH															16	18	20
3½ INCH																18	20	24
4 INCH																18	20	24

WHEN YOU BUY SCREWS, SPECIFY (1) LENGTH, (2) GAUGE NUMBER, (3) TYPE OF HEAD—FLAT, ROUND, OR OVAL, (4) MATERIAL—STEEL, BRASS, BRONZE, ETC., (5) FINISH—BRIGHT, STEEL BLUED, CADMIUM, NICKEL, OR CHROMIUM PLATED.

Contents

Power-train troubleshooting

■ THE POWER TRAIN of cars with rear-wheel drive consists of an engine, clutch and manual transmission, or automatic transmission, propeller shaft, universal joints, and rear-drive train composed of a differential, axle shafts and axle-shaft bearings. In a discussion of power-train noise, front suspension and tire/wheel assemblies, although not parts of the power train, have to be considered.

The power train of cars with front-wheel drive consists of an engine and a front transaxle made up of a clutch and manual transmission, or an automatic transmission, front differential drive-shafts and shaft bearings. There are no propeller shaft, universal joints or rear-drive train. However, tire/wheel assemblies, although not parts of the power train, have to be considered when discussing noise problems.

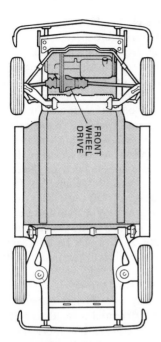

FRONT-WHEEL DRIVE cars lack drive shaft, all power train components are up front

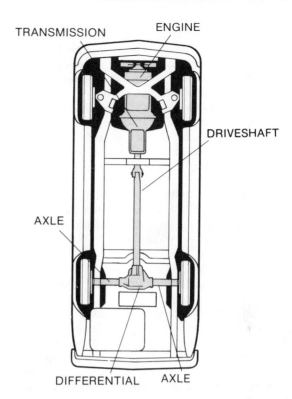

There are thousands of individual parts contained in the power trains of a rear-wheel or front-wheel-drive vehicle. Most parts emit noise when they fail. However, trying to put a finger on the problem area is frequently difficult because power-train noise is elusive.

For example, noise that seems to be coming from the rear-drive train of a rear-wheel-drive automobile may, in fact, be coming from the propeller shaft, transmission, tires or even the engine. Making snap judgments can lead to unnecessary, expensive repairs. Finding the source is the most important step in correcting a noise condition.

Troubleshooting power-train noise is a job you can do yourself, and procedures outlined here are intended to help. However, repairs are another matter.

In some instances, you should be able to make repairs yourself, as you will see by reviewing the repair information. In other cases, repairs cannot be made without doing a major overhaul.

Troubleshooting rear-drive train noise

The majority of noise complaints deal with suspected rear-drive train noise in rear-wheel-drive cars. The following procedure will help determine if the noise you hear is coming from the rear or elsewhere:

1. Remove the rear axle (differential) filler hole plug. If the plug is recessed, use a special wrench available from a parts and accessories dealer.

2. Check the differential lubricant level by inserting your pinkie. Lube should be no more than ½-inch below the filler hole. Add lubricant, if necessary.

Use only lubricant recommended by the manufacturer (consult the maintenance guide in the service manual). Recommendations differ according to climate (lighter-weight lubricants for colder climates) and the type of differential. Antispin (positraction) rear axles require an additive or special lubricant. A suction-type lubricating gun can be obtained to fill and drain differentials.

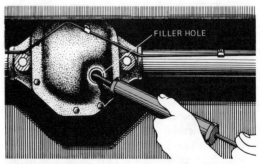

SUCTION-TYPE lubricating gun is used to fill and drain differentials.

3. Find a smooth tar or asphalt road, and drive the car for 20 minutes to warm up the differential. Then start from a stop, increasing speed gradually. Note the speedometer or tachometer reading at which noise is loudest.

4. Analyze the noise. Differential gear noise is most pronounced when the car is accelerating, cruising or coasting 30–40 mph and 50–60 mph. If noise isn't heard at these speeds, dismiss malfunctioning rear-axle gears as the source.

Differentials make some noise, which automotive engineers call the "commercially acceptable noise level." This light sound—more like a tone than a noise—is normal. It occurs within a narrow band between 40 and 60 mph. If the tone is there, it's going to stay there.

Rear-axle shaft bearing noise is a growl or grating sound. However, a bad front-wheel bearing sounds the same.

To pinpoint the source of a bad bearing, accelerate the car to 55 mph, turn off the ignition and shift the transmission to neutral. Swerve the car from side to side, so the load on the rear switches from one wheel to the other. If the growling or grating noise becomes amplified, a bad rear-axle shaft bearing exists.

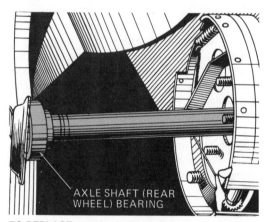

AXLE SHAFT (REAR WHEEL) BEARING

TO REPLACE an axle-shaft bearing, unhook and slide shaft from differential.

Confirm the existence of front-wheel bearing noise by jacking up the front wheels. Spin each wheel and listen for noise. Shake the wheels. A loose wheel indicates a loose (noisy) front-wheel bearing.

5. With the car standing still, and the transmission in neutral, increase engine speed until it reaches the range at which the noise was loudest during the road test. If you hear noise, look to the engine or exhaust system as the source.

6. To check the clutch, keep the transmission in neutral, run engine speed up to the noise range as you engage and disengage the clutch. If you hear noise, a bad clutch part probably exists.

7. To check on the transmission as a cause of noise, disconnect the propeller shaft from the transmission output shaft and increase engine speed to the noise range, with the transmission in high gear. Noise? Look in the transmission.

8. Noise made by tires can be distinguished from rear-axle noise by driving the car on a different road surface. If the pitch changes, tires are the noisemakers. If the pitch stays the same, suspect the rear axle. You can also check tires by temporarily increasing tire pressure to 50 pounds. Noise made by tires will be noticeably altered, but rear-axle noise will continue as before.

Rear-drive train repair

If lubricant level is low because of a leak around the differential cover, do not drive the car until repairs are made. Low lubricant is the main cause of differential failure.

To repair a leaking case caused by a bad gasket, do this:

1. Disconnect the propeller shaft from the differential universal-joint flange (see below, *Replacing a universal joint*).

2. Remove the differential cover bolts. Place a pan under the differential to catch lubricant and snap the cover loose.

3. Clean the flanges of the differential case and cover. Remove all pieces of old gasket material and sealer. When flanges are clean, wipe them dry.

4. Apply gasket sealer to the flange of the differential case and press on the gasket. Then apply

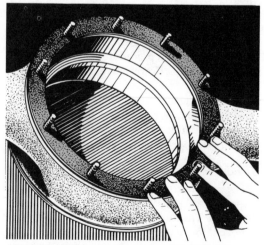

APPLY SEALER and press new gasket firmly into place; install cover.

sealer to the face of the gasket. Install the cover and torque bolts to the specification in the service manual, which is probably 25–30 foot-pounds.

Rear-axle overhaul and replacement of axle bearings are jobs most people leave to a mechanic. However, before having a mechanic replace ring and pinion gears, be certain rear axle noise isn't being made by a worn drive pinion bearing. Replacing the ring and pinion costs about $150 more than replacing a drive pinion bearing.

If the mechanic replaces the ring and pinion, the pinion backlash should also be adjusted. Excessive or insufficient backlash causes early failure. Generally, a ring-to-pinion backlash adjustment of .005 to .009 inch is called for. Backlash is adjusted by adding or subtracting shims, or by adjusting nuts.

Propeller shaft, U-joints

A bad propeller shaft won't make noise, but causes vehicle vibration. Universal joints that are about to fail emit a clunking noise, which is apparent at low speeds.

To verify that a universal joint is going bad, drive the car between 5 and 10 mph with the transmission in high gear. If clunking is pronounced, put the car on a lift and grasp the propeller shaft near each universal joint. Try rocking the shaft back and forth. It should not move.

If there is play in the shaft, tighten the universal joint flange bolts and do another road test. If noise isn't caused by loose flange bolts, replace the universal joint. Driving a car with a bad universal joint will eventually cause the propeller shaft to break loose, possibly causing loss of control.

Replacing a universal joint

1. Raise the car.

2. Use a file to scribe a mark across the rear universal joint flange and the differential companion flange. This is done to assure correct propeller shaft alignment when the shaft is reinstalled.

3. Remove the propeller shaft by removing the rear universal joint flange bolts and sliding the shaft off the transmission output shaft.

4. Place the propeller shaft on a workbench with the end possessing the suspected defective universal joint mounted in a vise. Do not tighten the vice forcefully, since you may damage the shaft. Use it to hold the shaft steady. Place the other end of the shaft on supports to keep the shaft level.

5. If the universal joint bearing cap has a snap-ring retainer, pull the retainer out with a pair of long-nose pliers. Tap around the outside of the bearing cap with a hammer until the cap pops loose. Slide the universal joint from the propeller shaft yoke.

If the universal joint bearing cap does not have a snap-ring connector, get a piece of pipe large enough to encircle the cap. Place the pipe over the cap and hit the end of the pipe with a hammer. This breaks the bearing cap retainer loose, forcing the retainer and cap from the propeller shaft yoke. Rotate the propeller shaft and remove the other cap, using the same method. When the two bearing caps have been removed, slide the universal joint cross assembly from the propeller shaft yoke.

6. Install the new universal joint by sliding the cross assembly into the propeller shaft yoke. Press on the bearing caps. Then, seat the caps securely by tapping them in place with a soft-faced hammer.

7. Install the propeller shaft, seeing that the reference mark on the universal joint flange lines up with the reference mark on the differential companion flange. Install and tighten the universal joint flange bolts as tightly as possible.

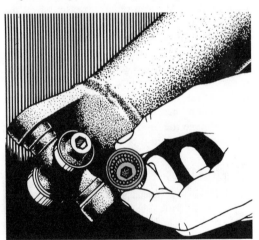

INSIDES of caps have bearings that are weak link of U-joint assemblies.

Noisy automatic transmission

Noise from an automatic transmission usually indicates the need for repair. However, as with differential gear noise, automatic transmissions emit a "commercially acceptable noise level." This noise is a low-key whine that increases in intensity as the car accelerates in first gear. Once the transmission shifts to a higher gear, the pitch of the whine drops.

UP FRONT, draw propeller shaft to rear, away from transmission shaft.

Noise other than a low-pitch whine is not normal. This includes a click, knock, scrape or shrill whine. The noise may be coming from the vacuum modulator or torque converter.

A word about modulators

If a vacuum modulator valve is present in your transmission, it is screwed into the transmission housing and connected to the carburetor by a vacuum tube. Most automatic transmissions use a vacuum modulator valve.

A modulator valve that fails causes the transmission to shift harshly or erratically and may produce noise. Since a modulator valve is relatively inexpensive, replace it at the first sign of transmission trouble. If you are lucky, no further repair will be necessary.

To replace the modulator valve, raise the car, remove the vacuum tube and unscrew the modulator valve and spring-and-pin assembly. Retain the spring-and-pin assembly to use with the new modulator valve. When the new valve has been installed, check the automatic transmission fluid level, since some fluid may have been lost when you removed the old valve.

Torque converters

A loose or cracked torque converter can make a knocking, clicking or scraping noise. Isolate noise to the converter by raising the car, placing the transmission in gear and having someone accelerate the engine to simulate the speed at which noise occurs. Place your ear at the torque converter and then at the transmission to pinpoint the source.

If it is the torque converter, remove the converter cover. Make sure converter plate bolts are tight. Rotate the converter plate and look for cracks in the plate. Replace a cracked one.

Noise inside the transmission indicates the unit will have to be overhauled.

Clutch noise

The purpose of a clutch is to disconnect the engine from the transmission as gears are being shifted, and to permit the engine to start and run. If an engine remained coupled to the transmission, it wouldn't attain starting speed because of resistance imposed by the transmission. A running engine in a stationary car must remain detached from the transmission, or the resistance imposed on the engine by the transmission will cause the engine to stall.

When the clutch is engaged and the car is put in motion, the clutch employs friction to drive the engine and transmission as a unit. A pressure

PULL bearing cap snap-ring retainers, if present, to release hold on U-joint.

TRANSMISSION vacuum modulator valve is often cause of many shifting problems.

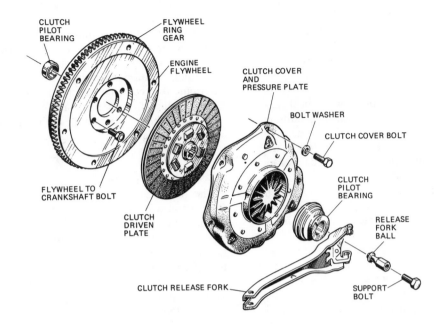

CLUTCH PILOT BEARING

FLYWHEEL RING GEAR

ENGINE FLYWHEEL

CLUTCH COVER AND PRESSURE PLATE

BOLT WASHER

CLUTCH COVER BOLT

CLUTCH PILOT BEARING

RELEASE FORK BALL

FLYWHEEL TO CRANKSHAFT BOLT

CLUTCH DRIVEN PLATE

CLUTCH RELEASE FORK

SUPPORT BOLT

plate and a clutch disc are the two main parts of a clutch assembly. The pressure plate is attached to the engine flywheel, while the clutch disc is located between the flywheel and pressure plate. The clutch disc drives the clutch shaft, also called the throwout bearing shaft. It couples the clutch and transmission.

The clutch disc is the key element. It possesses a layer of friction material on both sides. When the clutch is engaged, heavy torsion springs force the clutch disc, flywheel and pressure plate firmly together. The three parts act as one as they rotate. Engine torque is thus able to be transmitted from the flywheel, through the clutch, to the transmission.

When the clutch is disengaged (clutch pedal depressed), a part called the clutch fork applies pressure to a clutch release bearing (also called the throwout bearing). This bearing rotates against, and puts pressure on, the clutch release levers. The clutch release levers, in turn, compress clutch springs. This action forces the pressure plate to the rear, disengaging the pressure plate from the flywheel. The two then rotate independently, as the clutch disc and clutch shaft become stationary.

There are several different kinds of clutches, but all work pretty much the same. A major difference is whether they are dry or wet.

Dry clutches, which have graphite coatings that act as a lubricant, are used in cars and light trucks. Some dry clutches, especially those in imported vehicles, employ a hydraulic assist that acts similarly to the booster of a power braking system.

One type of hydraulic assist forces fluid from a master cylinder into the clutch housing. The oil presses against a piston, which applies pressure to a series of discs that are connected to the clutch disc. The disc turns and power is transmitted to the transmission.

Heavier vehicles generally use a wet clutch, which should not be confused with clutches employing hydraulic assist. Wet clutches supply oil to the clutch for lubrication.

Clutch problems

Noise coming from the clutch usually warns of a broken or rough-running component, such as a pitted or chewed-up throwout bearing, broken clutch lever or fork, broken torsion spring, cracked or loose clutch disc. To resolve clutch noise, and the problem it suggests, the assembly must be overhauled or replaced.

Most clutch problems involve a clutch that slips or drags. A clutch that slips is characterized by car speed that doesn't keep pace with engine speed. The car lacks power, especially when going uphill.

To determine if a clutch is slipping, park the car on level ground and let the engine idle. Set the parking brake, depress the clutch pedal and shift the transmission into first gear. Press down on the accelerator pedal gradually while you slowly release the clutch pedal. The engine should stall. If the engine doesn't stall, the clutch is slipping. A slipping clutch is caused by lack of clutch pedal freeplay, worn clutch disc face, oil- or grease-contaminated clutch disc face, weak clutch springs, or pressure plate or flywheel run-out. Runout refers to a nonconcentric condition.

Clutch pedal free-play adjustment is the only service a clutch requires. Free play refers to the amount of movement in the clutch pedal before the clutch disc engages.

Wear of the clutch disc is normal. As a clutch disc wears, the amount of free play is reduced. If specified free play isn't maintained, wear will be hastened.

Free play should be adjusted periodically, as specified by the maker. The adjustment differs from car to car, so see your service manual.

A dragging clutch makes noise. To determine if a clutch is dragging, keep the clutch pedal pressed to the floor and press the accelerator pedal halfway. Shift into gear. If there is a grinding noise, the clutch is dragging.

Clutch drag is caused by excessive free play, weak or worn torsion springs, bad throwout bearing or a warped clutch disc.

Noisy manual transmissions

A noisy manual transmission often signifies a problem requiring major overhaul. A gear or bearing may be broken, or the main shaft spline could be worn.

Manual transmission noise could also mean that there isn't enough lubricant in the gearbox.

Many owners don't pay attention to the lubrication requirements of a manual transmission. This is a mistake. A manual transmission should be kept filled with lubricant of the correct viscosity to avert damage.

Consult the lubrication guide for your car to determine the recommended lubricant. Remove the filler plug of the transmission case. If lubricant level is below the bottom of the filler hole, add sufficient lubricant to bring the level to the bottom of the hole.

Front-wheel-drive noise

The presence of noise in the front axle of front-wheel-drive vehicles is normally confirmed by the presence of an instability and/or steering-wheel shimmy condition. Noises are usually grinding or grating sounds, which distinguish them from engine noise.

The most common causes of noise in the front axle assembly are:
• Worn, loose or seized driveshaft ball joint.
• Worn, loose or seized wheel bearing.
• Too much play in the driveshaft and differential side gear serrations.
• Too much play in the driveshaft and hub serrations.

Noise and accompanying instability and/or steering-wheel shimmy normally mean the front axle has to be overhauled. However, before doing this make sure your mechanic determines that the noise is not the result of a front suspension problem. Lubricate the chassis. If this doesn't get rid of noise, check the strut suspension components (coil springs and bushings) for damage.

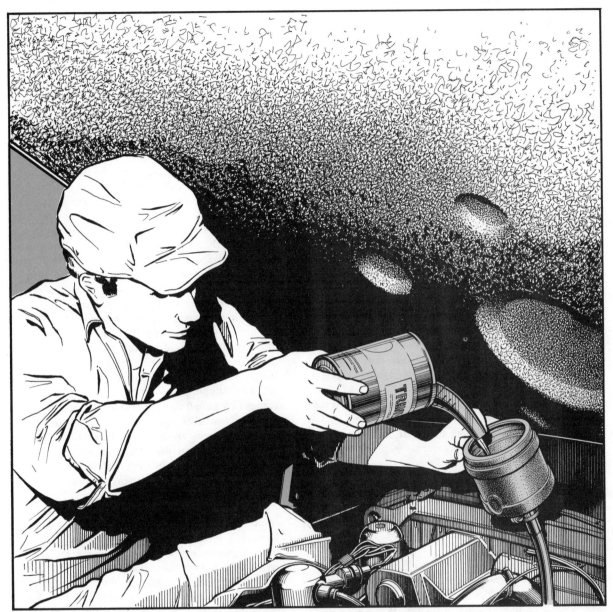

CHECKING FLUID LEVEL regularly and replenishing when necessary is vital for long automatic transmission life.

Automatic transmission service

■ DOES AUTOMATIC TRANSMISSION maintenance pay? "Not usually," say the automakers. "Absolutely," say transmission repair shops.

Since the early 1970s, carmakers have dismissed regular A/T maintenance as a waste of time and money for cars that are driven under normal conditions. For example, Chrysler and Ford contend that it never has to be done. GM says to do it once every 100,000 miles.

GM says durability tests prove that given the quality of present-day transmission fluids, maintenance beyond what is recommended in GM maintenance schedules will not prolong the life of a transmission.

Those who run transmission repair shops don't always agree. They contend that servicing every 20,000 miles helps extend transmission life in several ways. First, you are able to determine if a problem has developed that could, if not treated, lead to extensive damage. Second, as fluid is drained, small particles that can slip through the filter and enter the heart of the transmission to hasten wear are also drained. Third, some of the new compact transmission filters eventually clog and need replacement. Finally, owners may not be aware that the way they use their cars is considered "severe" by automakers. Scheduled maintenance will provide the needed protection.

'Severe' versus 'normal'

There is no disagreement that high temperature brought about by severe usage causes A/T fluid to oxidize and its additives to break down, and car manufacturers encourage transmission maintenance under these conditions. Chrysler and GM, for example, recommend service every 15,000 miles—Ford every 20,000 to 22,500 miles—in vehicles that are subjected to severe usage. They define severe usage as follows:
• Vehicles used more than half the time in city traffic when the temperature is 90°F. or more.
• Vehicles that tow trailers.
• Vehicles operated in dusty areas.
• Vehicles driven frequently on hills and mountains.
• Vehicles that are used for taxi, police, limousine or commercial operation.

Early detection

By performing regular A/T service, you may detect a developing transmission problem early enough to save a lot of money. When you drop the transmission pan to drain fluid, you can see if brass or white metal particles are present; then you can replace the affected part before the damage progresses past the danger point.

It's important to remember that there will always be some clutch material in the bottom of a transmission pan and that this does not necessarily indicate excessive wear. With some cars, a small amount of powdered brass may even be considered normal.

More than one car owner has been talked into unnecessary repairs after being shown a transmission pan that contained only normal wear material.

Automatic transmission service

Here are the steps to follow for periodic A/T service:

1. Warm the transmission to operating temperature, shut off the engine, and raise the car. If you've put a drain plug in the pan, place stands under the front wheels and chocks behind the rear wheels. This way, the pan is pitched toward the rear so the fluid will drain freely. Drain plug or not, you'll be working under the car, so make sure it's securely supported.

2. Place a drain pan under the transmission and loosen bolts holding the pan in place. If you don't have a drain plug, drop one corner of the pan lower than the others and allow it to drain (see Fig. 1). Once the flow stops, remove the remaining bolts, being careful not to spill the fluid still in the pan. *Caution:* Be careful not to get fluid in your eyes. Wear eye protection.

3. When the pan is down, examine the fluid left in it. It should be red. If it's dirty and smells like varnish, the fluid is worn out and has oxidized. If the fluid oxidation is accompanied by large deposits of clutch material, it may be the result of slipping clutches. Any condition that causes excessive fluid temperature can cause oxidation. Remember, some clutch wear is normal.

Severe usage can cause fluid oxidation. The installation of an auxiliary transmission oil cooler can help prevent overheating that occurs due to trailer towing, mountain driving or other severe use.

If the fluid looks milky, the transmission oil cooler has sprung a leak and coolant is mixing with A/T fluid. Drain coolant as well as A/T fluid. Remove the radiator and have a radiator repair shop replace the cooler.

Continue fluid inspection by holding the pan to sunlight or shining a light over it. See if you can spot white metal or brass particles. If you find them, you can have the transmission disassembled and the deteriorating part replaced before it leads to more extensive damage, or you can gamble that greater damage won't occur—it may not.

4. Strip the old gasket from the transmission and pan (Fig. 2). Then wash the pan in a nonflammable solvent.

5. Remove the filter (Figs. 3 and 4). Discard and replace a paper or felt filter. Clean a metal filter in solvent and reuse it. When you install the filter, make screws snug without overtightening them.

6. Place a new gasket on the transmission pan

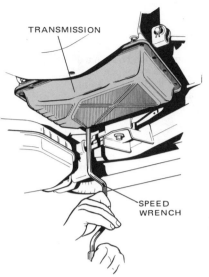

1. TO DRAIN TRANSMISSION PAN, loosen bolts that hold the pan to the transmission body and lower one corner of the pan.

Move the transmission shift lever slowly through the shifting pattern, stopping for a few seconds at each gear. Check fluid level again and, if necessary, add fluid to bring the level back to FULL.

There are two important facts you should be aware of. First, dirt is an A/T's worst enemy. Take steps to see that none is introduced into the transmission through the dipstick tube. Second, don't overfill the transmission. Excess fluid can cause the transmission to slip.

To make sure you haven't botched up and caused a fluid leak, keep an eye on the fluid level

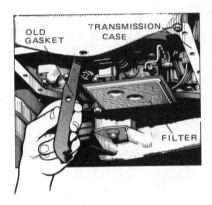

2. STRIP ALL OF THE OLD GASKET from the transmission body and pan. Use a scraper if necessary.

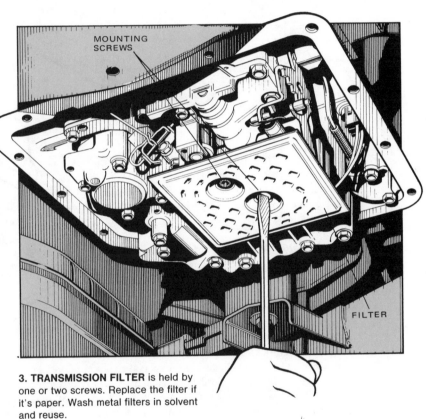

3. TRANSMISSION FILTER is held by one or two screws. Replace the filter if it's paper. Wash metal filters in solvent and reuse.

(Fig. 5) and carefully lay the pan against the transmission case so the gasket doesn't crimp or tear. Install bolts fingertight. Then, using a wrench, tighten bolts snugly in an alternating pattern. Do not overtighten. You may crush the gasket and cause a leak.

7. Remove the A/T fluid dipstick and place a clean funnel in the dipstick tube. Add fluid, a quart or two at a time. Reinstall the dipstick each time to get a reading until the fluid level shows FULL. Start the engine and let it get warm.

4. METAL PARTICLES on the back of this filter could have circulated through the transmission, causing unnecessary wear.

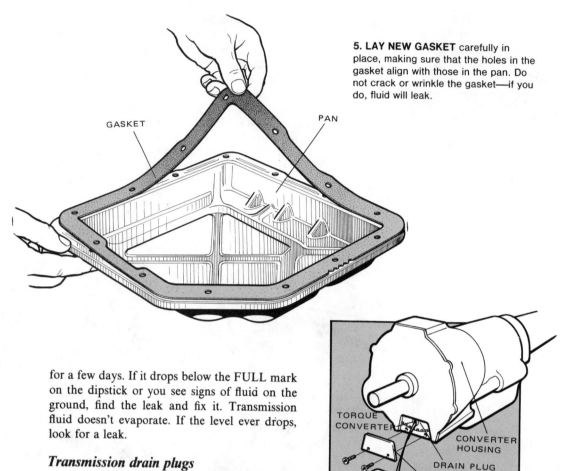

5. LAY NEW GASKET carefully in place, making sure that the holes in the gasket align with those in the pan. Do not crack or wrinkle the gasket—if you do, fluid will leak.

GASKET

PAN

TORQUE CONVERTER

CONVERTER HOUSING

DRAIN PLUG

ACCESS PLATE

DRAIN PAN

6. MOST FORDS have torque converter drain plugs, which allow you to empty the converter for a complete change.

for a few days. If it drops below the FULL mark on the dipstick or you see signs of fluid on the ground, find the leak and fix it. Transmission fluid doesn't evaporate. If the level ever drops, look for a leak.

Transmission drain plugs

When you drop the transmission pan to drain fluid, only some of the fluid pours out. A considerable amount remains in the torque converter. Most torque converters don't have drain plugs. To drain all of the fluid remaining in the torque converter, the transmission and torque converter have to be removed from the car and the converter has to be power-flushed on a special machine. Generally, many Ford-built cars have a torque converter drain plug. GM models don't, and neither do most Chrysler-built cars from 1977 on.

There is a way around this problem, but first find out if there is a drain plug in your torque converter. Look for an access plate on the converter housing. Unscrew the attachment bolts and remove the plate. Then, have someone in the car click the starter motor in short bursts to see if a drain plug comes into view. (Keep the engine from starting by disconnecting the ignition coil.) If the torque converter has a drain plug, remove it to drain all the fluid (Fig. 6).

Even if your car doesn't have a drain plug in the torque converter you can still do a good job

of removing dirty fluid and replenishing additives with two or three successive pan drainings and refills. Installing a plug in the pan will allow you to do this easily. To install a universal drain plug, drop the pan, pour off fluid and wash the pan in solvent. Drill a ½-inch hole near a rear corner of the pan.

Clean off all burrs and bolt the fitting through the ½-inch hole. Screw the drain plug into the fitting (Fig. 7) and reinstall the pan. Make the plug secure, but don't overtighten it or you'll damage the plug or fitting.

Pour in enough fresh A/T fluid to fill the transmission. Drive the car for a day or two, so fresh fluid mixes with the old fluid that was

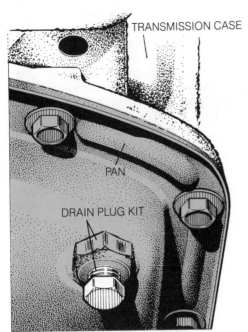

7. INSTALLING A DRAIN PLUG on the pan will let you dilute and drain most of the dirty fluid from the torque converter.

trapped in the torque converter. Then unscrew the new transmission drain plug and allow the fluid to drain. Refill the transmission and repeat this filling-driving-draining procedure two or three times to replace most of the old fluid with new fluid. Of course, you will still have to remove the pan to inspect or replace the filter.

Band adjustment

Should transmission bands be adjusted as part of a servicing program? That depends. Most GM transmissions are nonadjustable—bands are adjusted automatically. Manufacturers of transmissions that have adjustable bands stipulate that an adjustment is not necessary unless the transmission is used under severe conditions. Ford, for example, calls for an adjustment on some vehicles every 7500 miles when severe usage is evident. However, if you follow a periodic maintenance program with a transmission that's used under normal conditions, it's usually not necessary to adjust bands.

Transmissions that call for a band adjustment usually have an adjustment mechanism on the outside of the transmission housing that tightens the front bands. The rear band adjustment mechanism is usually inside the transmission, and in many cases you have to remove the valve body to reach it. Bands should be adjusted to manufacturer specification, which is normally given in inch-pounds. A torque wrench and a shop manual are needed.

Vacuum modulators

In some cars—those made by Chrysler, for example—the linkage or cable between the carburetor and transmission allows the car to respond to driving demands. This linkage usually needs no adjustment unless the transmission is removed from the car.

The other control, used primarily by GM and Ford, is a vacuum modulator. If there is a sudden change in the way the transmission shifts, pull

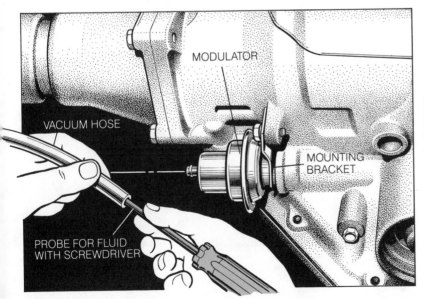

8. TO TEST A VACUUM MODULATOR for leaks, remove the vacuum hose and look for fluid inside. The hose should be dry. If it's wet, unscrew or unbolt modulator and replace it.

the vacuum line from the vacuum modulator, which is on the side of the transmission (Fig. 8). If A/T fluid drips out, you've uncovered the trouble and, luckily, can make an inexpensive repair. The modulation diaphragm has failed, so replace the modulator. Other signs that the modulator has gone bad are a drop in fluid level and white or gray engine exhaust smoke. Also, make certain that the vacuum line is not leaking at the other end where it connects to the carburetor.

Choosing fluid

It's important to follow the manufacturer's recommendation for the type of A/T fluid, since improper fluid may cause malfunctions. Ford calls for Type H fluid to be used in its C5 transmission. Otherwise, manufacturers recommend either Dexron II or Type F. Check your owner's manual before you add or replace fluid. If you can't find the information in your owner's manual, look it up in a shop manual or ask a mechanic at a dealership or transmission shop. Be sure you know the transmission model and year of manufacture. Some carmakers (like Ford) use Type F fluid in older models and Dexron II in new ones.

If you service your automatic transmission periodically, it should never let you down. You are less likely to be victimized by an unscrupulous transmission shop if you can shop around, rather than having to settle for the most convenient shop after a breakdown.

Cable-operated shifter adjustments

■ WITH THE ADVENT of transverse-mounted engines in front-wheel-drive cars, many things have changed. However, some mechanical systems which were long ago abandoned by automakers have been reclaimed because they happen to be suited to this new type of drivetrain.

One such item is the cable-operated gearshifter. The cable shifter that we knew many years ago was a cantankerous device connecting a pair of shift levers on the bottom of the shift column to the transmission. It rarely stayed in

GEARSHIFTING CABLES used on front-wheel-drive transaxles may require occasional adjustment to cure rough shifting problems. Typical setup uses trans-shifter cable and trans-selector cable.

LEVER-G

NUT-E

LOCKING PIN-H

LEVER-F

NUT-E

CABLE-A

CABLE-B

SHIFTER ASSEMBLY

adjustment and gave a rubbery feel to shifts. Later, we saw the cables emerge again in automatic transmission selectors including some of the Chrysler pushbutton units of the '50s and '60s.

But certain designs tend to resurface in the car business because old mechanisms can sometimes solve new problems. So, today many carmakers have adapted cable mechanisms to their front-wheel-drive designs.

There is an up side to the story. The cable shifter allows flexibility of design in new cars. Due to the placement of the engine and transaxle in a front-wheel-drive car, linkage shifting devices on the manual units can present unusual problems. Because of the torque reaction movement of the engine and transaxle, a solid linkage shifter must move with the engine and trans or the trans will jump out of gear. Some automakers, like Ford and Honda, tie the shifter to the transaxle and use a solid linkage. This leaves you with a shaking shifter but, under normal conditions, no adjustment is necessary.

GM and Chrysler have evidently decided that a shaky shifter is unacceptable. GM has two cable-type shifters—one for the four-speed and one for the five. Chrysler uses rod shifters (with pivot points that allow engine movement) on some transaxles and a cable shifter on others. While these shifters do present some compromises, they can function well if they're properly lubricated and adjusted.

In the following paragraphs, we'll explain how you can keep your GM or Chrysler manual transmission shifter shifting slickly.

GENERAL MOTORS

General Motors uses cable shifters on its front-wheel-drive X- and J-body cars. Two different shifters are used—one for the four-speed and one for the five-speed. The shifter is mounted to the floorboard of the car and all the workings of the

shifter are located inside the passenger compartment. There is little danger of affecting the shifter end of the cables.

Two cables extend from the shifter itself to the transmission. One cable is called the trans-selector cable, while the other is described as the trans-shifter cable. For service procedure information, they are simply referred to as cables A and B. Cable B is closest to the driver where it attaches to the shift lever, and it passes through the firewall to the left of cable A. On the four-speed transaxle, cable B is attached to a vertical "select" lever and is toward the front of the vehicle. Cable A is behind it and is attached to a horizontal "shift" lever.

On the five-speed transaxle, cable A is connected to a shift lever that GM calls lever F. It's a vertical lever that hangs down alongside the transaxle case. Cable B is connected to an odd-shaped lever G that moves horizontally.

In order to shift correctly, the shift cables must be properly adjusted. If the adjustment is okay and there is still a hang-up in the 1-2 shift, it may be necessary to replace the shifter shaft selective washer with one of a different thickness. This washer helps position the shifter shaft for minimum shift effort.

Adjustment of the shifter and cables can be done quite simply on most GM cars, but the procedure is different for the two manual transaxles in use. The first step for both transaxles is the removal of the negative battery cable.

Four-speed adjustment

Cable adjustments are made at the transaxle end of the cable, but you will need access to both ends of the cables. The shifter cables are attached to the studs in the transmission shifter levers by a couple of clips. The studs are inserted through slotted holes in the shifter levers and are secured with nuts. If the nuts are loosened, the studs will

1. NUT E, on the threaded stud which attaches the cable to the transaxle lever, must be loosened to make alignments. Lever holes are slotted so stud will slide.

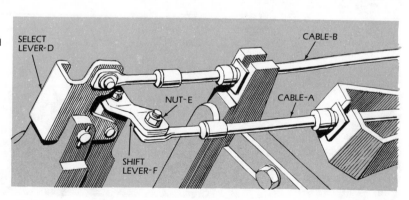

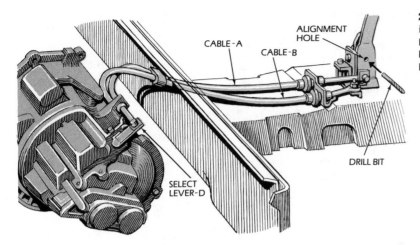

2. A 5/32-INCH DRILL BIT inserted into the alignment hole at the shifter base (shown) will lock the gearshift lever in FIRST, allowing the cables to be adjusted as required.

slide back and forth in their mounting slots. This movement is the means of adjustment. From under the hood, loosen the nuts so the studs will slide in the slots (Fig. 1).

Next, remove the center console or boot that covers the shifter. This may involve removing the console cover or trim plate, peeling back the shifter boot toward the top of the shifter, locating the screws that hold the console in place and removing them. The console slides out easier if the shifter is in FIRST.

On the side of the gearshift lever, down near the base, you will probably find a 5/32-in. alignment hole (Fig. 2). The hole goes through the base of the shifter that mounts to the floor. With the gears in FIRST or LOW, slide a 5/32-in. drill bit through the holes. This aligns the shifter in a known position. Next, have a helper hold the shift handle to the left toward the driver. Some late models may not have alignment holes. In this case, have your helper simply hold the shift lever in FIRST and apply pressure so that it is as close to the driver as possible.

With the shifter locked in position, locate the shifter select lever and remove lash by pushing it toward the driver's side of the car. With the lever held in position, tighten up the nuts on the cable-mounting stud. A bit of caution here: Don't loosen the nut any more than needed to allow the stud to slide and, when tightening the nut, take care not to lose the adjustment you have just made.

Adjust the shift lever in a similar manner. Push against the lever in such a way that all of the slack in the cable and its connections is taken up before retightening the nut.

The idea behind this is that you'll end up with a tight cable, shifter and lever assembly. When

the shifter is moved to change gears, you'll get an immediate reaction at the transaxle.

Once the adjustment is made, remove the drill bit from the alignment hole (if used). Work the shifter through all of the gears and check its operation. If it does not feel right, run through the adjustment procedure again. If the shift still doesn't feel right, you will have to check the cables for binding. To do this, remove them from the transmission end and the shifter. Work the cable by hand and replace the cable if there are rough spots.

If you find that the shifter hangs up between FIRST and SECOND even after the adjustment is okay, a change may be needed in the size of the spacer washer at the base of the gearshift stick. This is fairly complicated and you really need a depth micrometer and tension gauge to do it correctly. If you have these tools and a shop manual, you may want to attempt it. If not, ask your dealer to check for proper shift selective washer size as described in section 7B1 of most GM manuals.

Five-speed adjustment

As with the four-speed, begin by disconnecting the negative battery cable. Then, shift the transaxle to THIRD gear. On the transaxle, directly in front of the two shift levers, you'll find a locking pin consisting of a stud and a set screw that are threaded into the trans case (Fig. 3). Remove this locking pin and reinsert it with the tapered end down. This will lock the trans in THIRD.

Loosen the shift-cable attaching nuts at shift levers G and F (on the transaxle). After removing the console or shifter boot, install a 5/32-in. or No. 22 drill bit into the alignment hole at the side of the shifter handle (Fig. 4).

There's another hole in the shifter assembly close to where cable B attaches to the shift mechanism. Align the hole in the shift lever with the hole in the bracket and insert a 3/16-in. drill bit.

Now, with both drill bits holding the shifter in the correct position, tighten the nuts on levers G and F. Remove the lockpin and reinstall it with the tapered end up. Reinstall the console and battery cable and road test the vehicle. If the shifter doesn't have a good neutral gate feel— that is, if you can't move the stick back and forth laterally while it's in NEUTRAL—readjust the shifter mechanism and test it again.

Once the adjustment is completed, lubricate the moving parts of the shift mechanism with white lithium grease. Use a stiff-bristled, small brush to apply the grease to the parts. (This

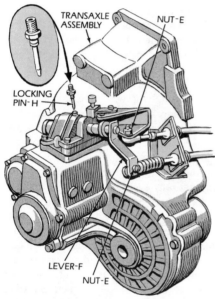

3. ON THE GM FIVE-SPEED transmission, locking pin H must be reinstalled tapered end down to lock the trans in THIRD gear.

should be applied to both four- and five-speed shifters.)

If the transmission still does not shift right after all of the adjustments have been made, the shifter has been lubed and (on four-speeds) the size of the selective washer is correct, the transmission will have to come out of the car for further service.

CHRYSLER

Here are the adjustment procedures for three transmissions used in Chrysler front-wheel-drive

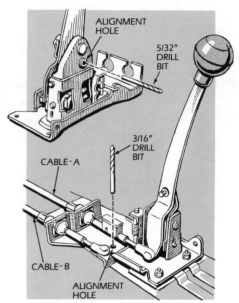

4. DRILL BITS inserted in both alignment holes permit five-speed shifter adjustment.

cars—the A-412 four-speed, the A-460 four-speed and the A-465 five-speed. The A-412 unit is linkage-operated while the A-460 and the A-465 could be either linkage or cable.

Identification of the three transmissions is easy. The A-412 has a two-piece case while the A-460 and A-465 have a one-piece case.

A-412 adjustment

To adjust the rod-type linkage on an A-412 transaxle, position the gearshift lever in NEUTRAL on the 3-4 side of the shifter gate. Find and loosen the clamp on the shifter rod that looks like an adjustment clamp on a tie rod.

Then, on the lower part of the shifter, find the two alignment marks (Fig. 5). One is on the blocker bracket—a hole—while the other—a U-shaped slot—is on the slider bracket. Align the tab or slot on the slider with the hole on the blocker bracket.

Make a ¾-in. spacer block and place it between the slider and the blocker bracket. Tighten the clamp on the shift tube while pushing the slider toward the blocker, with the spacer sandwiched between them. If the bushings are okay, the pins in place and the shift tube not bent, this should result in a smooth shifting linkage.

Rod-operated A-460 and A-465

To adjust a rod-type shifter on either the A-460 manual four-speed or the A-465 five-speed, position the shifter on the 1-2 side of the neutral gate. Then, while leaning over the left front fender, find the selector-shaft housing on the transmission. On top of it, there is a 10-mm hex head locking pin that looks like a pointer screwed into the transaxle (Fig. 6). Remove this pin with a 10-mm wrench and reinstall it with the tapered end down. This will lock the selector shaft in the 1-2 NEUTRAL position.

Jack up the car and support it on jackstands with the rear wheels securely blocked and the

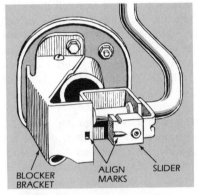

5. THE HOLE in the blocker bracket and the U-shaped slot on the slider must be aligned.

emergency brake applied. From under the car, loosen the clamp bolt that secures the gearshift tube to the gearshift connector. Make certain that the gearshift connector moves and slides freely. Then, align the hole in the blockout bracket with the rib on the isolator attached to the base of the

gearshift (Fig. 7). The isolator should be contacting the upstanding flange.

Hold the connector isolator in this position while tightening the clamp bolt on the gearshift tube to 170 in.-lb. Don't exert any force on any part of the linkage while tightening the clamp bolt.

Lower the vehicle and remove the lock pin from the selector shaft housing. Reinstall it with the long tapered end up and torque it to 105 in.-lb. Check to make sure the trans shifts well into FIRST and REVERSE and that it blocks out going into REVERSE.

A-460 and A-465 cable shifter

Before beginning this adjustment, make two adjusting pins as illustrated (Fig. 8). Each should be 5 x 5/32-in., and each should be bent into an L-shape to facilitate removal. (If you just use 5 x 5/32-in. drill bits, you may have trouble removing them.) Once you've made the adjustment pins, remove and reverse the lock pin that is screwed into the selector shaft housing in the same manner as described above for rod-type shifter adjustment. The shifter should be in the 1-2 side of the neutral gate.

Then, remove the gearshift lever knob and the pull-up ring under it. Remove the console assembly and shifter boot.

Loosen the crossover cable adjusting screw and the selector cable adjusting screw, and insert the adjusting pins into the shifter mechanism in the places indicated (Fig. 9). With the pins in place, the shifter will be in NEUTRAL on the 1-2 side of the gate.

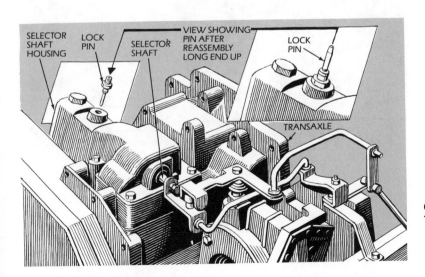

6. ON THE CHRYSLER A-460/465 TRANSAXLE, the locking pin must be removed and reinstalled with long tapered end down to lock the gearbox in NEUTRAL and allow shift rod alignment.

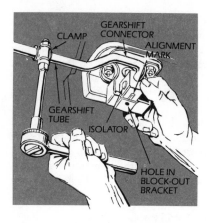

CLAMP
GEARSHIFT CONNECTOR
ALIGNMENT MARK
GEARSHIFT TUBE
ISOLATOR
HOLE IN BLOCK-OUT BRACKET

Leave the pins in place and retighten the selector cable-adjusting screw and the crossover cable-adjusting screw to 60 in.-lb.

Remove the lock pin from the selector shaft housing and reinstall it with the long tapered end up. Tighten the lock pin to 105 in.-lb. Check the shift into FIRST and REVERSE and the RE-VERSE blockout.

Smooth shifting

Shift cable adjustments should restore the alignment of moving parts so that the lever glides smoothly between the gears and will make the crossover between 1-2 and 3-4 gates without hang-up. In addition to making sure that the cable sheaths are routed in smooth arcs and the cables themselves are properly lubricated, you should look after the condition of any grommets or bushings where the cable attaches to the trans-axle and shifter assembly. If they are worn or distorted, replace with new, lubricated parts.

A little time spent on the shifter, if it is not working smoothly, could make all the difference between enjoying a car or complaining about it.

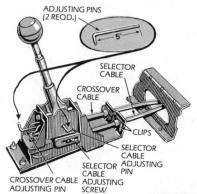

ADJUSTING PINS (2 REQD.)
5"
SELECTOR CABLE
CROSSOVER CABLE
CLIPS
SELECTOR CABLE ADJUSTING PIN
SELECTOR CABLE ADJUSTING SCREW
CROSSOVER CABLE ADJUSTING PIN

9. AFTER ADJUSTING PINS have been inserted, torque the crossover and the selector adjusting screws to 60 in.-lb. with a torque wrench and remove the adjusting pins.

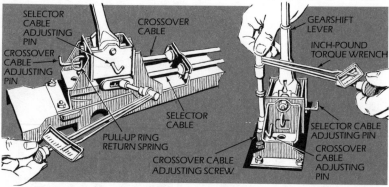

SELECTOR CABLE ADJUSTING PIN
CROSSOVER CABLE ADJUSTING PIN
CROSSOVER CABLE
GEARSHIFT LEVER
INCH-POUND TORQUE WRENCH
SELECTOR CABLE
PULL-UP RING RETURN SPRING
CROSSOVER CABLE ADJUSTING SCREW
SELECTOR CABLE ADJUSTING PIN
CROSSOVER CABLE ADJUSTING PIN

Differential trouble-shooting

■ THE DIFFERENTIAL is also known as the rear end or rear axle by those who drive rear-wheel-drive cars.

A front-wheel-drive car also has a differential, but you can't legitimately call it a rear end or rear axle since it isn't in the rear. It's up front along with the engine and transmission, and all three are coupled together in an integral unit called the transaxle.

The differential transmits power to a car's wheels by increasing torque from the power train. But that is only part of its job. This is the least important role performed by the differential.

In fact, if cars traveled only in a straight line, differentials wouldn't be needed. Power from the engine and transmission could be applied directly to the wheels through a geared driveshaft.

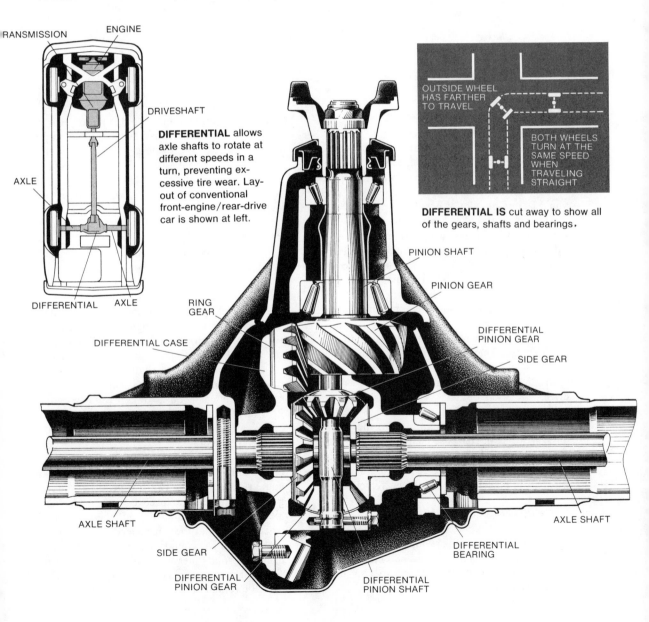

TRANSMISSION   ENGINE

DRIVESHAFT

DIFFERENTIAL allows axle shafts to rotate at different speeds in a turn, preventing excessive tire wear. Layout of conventional front-engine/rear-drive car is shown at left.

AXLE

DIFFERENTIAL   AXLE

OUTSIDE WHEEL HAS FARTHER TO TRAVEL

BOTH WHEELS TURN AT THE SAME SPEED WHEN TRAVELING STRAIGHT

DIFFERENTIAL IS cut away to show all of the gears, shafts and bearings.

PINION SHAFT

PINION GEAR

DIFFERENTIAL PINION GEAR

SIDE GEAR

RING GEAR

DIFFERENTIAL CASE

AXLE SHAFT

AXLE SHAFT

SIDE GEAR

DIFFERENTIAL PINION GEAR

DIFFERENTIAL PINION SHAFT

DIFFERENTIAL BEARING

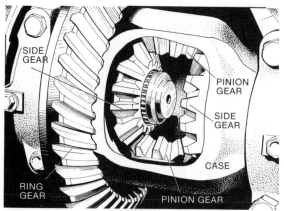

CONVENTIONAL differential, illustrated here, shows meshing of various gears as explained in the text.

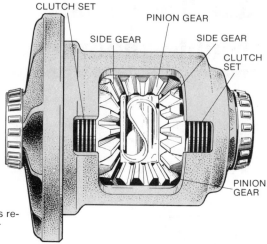

LIMITED-SLIP differential in this illustration shows relationship of the two clutch sets to all of the other components.

Why it's needed

But cars turn, making it necessary for an outside wheel to travel farther than an inside wheel. If there were no differential, the outside wheel would skid in an effort to keep up with the inside wheel. The car would be hard to control, and you'd be buying a lot of new tires.

The differential allows wheels to rotate at different speeds during a turn, permitting the outside wheel to catch up with the inside wheel.

In most cars, the rear end is connected to the transmission by a long shaft that revolves. The system consisting of this driveshaft and the differential and transmission is commonly referred to as the final drive.

In other cars, the rear end is connected directly to the engine. There is no driveshaft. This is true of cars having engines in the rear. It is also true, as mentioned before, of cars having front-wheel-drive.

No matter where that differential is located and no matter how it's connected to the transmission, it has the purpose mentioned here. Mechanically, though, it accomplishes these goals in a different way. This article deals with the way it does this in rear-drive, front-engine vehicles.

Conventional or limited-slip

Two kinds of differentials are made for rear-wheel-drive standard passenger cars: conventional and limited-slip. Limited-slip differentials are not used in front-wheel-drive cars and those having engines in the rear.

In a conventional differential, a pinion gear on the end of the pinion shaft (which is the output end of the driveshaft) meshes and turns with a large ring gear that is bolted to the differential case. A pinion is a gear with a small number of teeth that is designed to mesh with a larger gear or wheel.

How it works

The differential case rotates on the axle shafts by means of a bearing between the case and a shaft.

Two side gears, each connected to the differential case and attached to its individual axle shaft, exert power laterally through the axle shafts to the wheels. Other key parts of the differential are the two differential pinion gears. These are held by a differential pinion shaft in the differential case so they mesh with the two side gears.

When the car is on a straight run, the pinion gear turns the ring gear, which causes the differential case and all parts to turn as a unit without any relative motion.

The two differential pinion gears don't rotate on the differential pinion shaft, but they do exert equal pressure on the two side gears, so the side gears turn at the same speed as the ring gear. This allows both axle shafts, and therefore both wheels, to turn at the same speed.

When the car rounds a curve, the balance is disrupted. The inner wheel slows down, and the side gear to the inner axle shaft also slows down. The differential pinion gears start rotating on the differential pinion shaft because of this disruption in equilibrium, which allows more speed to be applied to the outside gear and, hence, to the outside axle shaft and wheel.

If the differential case speed represents 100 percent and the inner wheel slows to 90 percent of this speed, the outer wheel would respond by speeding at 110 percent.

A limited-slip differential differs from a conventional differential because of the addition of two sets of clutches, each serving one axle shaft. The purpose of the clutches is to lock the axle shafts to the differential case when either wheel hits ice or mud, which would cause the wheel to lose traction.

Locked in, the "tractionless" wheel can't spin since it cannot turn faster than the other wheel.

Clutches in some limited-slip differentials are not applied at all times, but lock up only when engine torque is applied. This keeps clutch plates from wearing on every turn, which extends their usefulness.

The operation of these torque units is sometimes misunderstood because on surfaces where unequal traction exists, the differential may allow a wheel to spin unless engine torque is applied. An effective way of avoiding this is to engage the parking brake lever two or three notches and accelerate, allowing the differential to lock up. If your car is equipped with a parking brake foot pedal, hold it down using light foot pressure and then accelerate.

To test the performance of a limited-slip differential without the torque feature, next time the car is on a lift, place an automatic transmission in PARK or a manual transmission in low gear. Grip the tire and try turning the wheel.

The differential is in good condition if it is very difficult, if not impossible, to turn the wheels. If either wheel turns easily, the limited-slip unit is not performing properly.

If the car has a limited-slip differential which locks under load (torque) only, a road test is necessary to judge performance. Make the test on a dry pavement, preferably asphalt. Accelerate from a dead stop at full throttle.

Go about 50 or 100 feet and stop the car. Check the pavement for signs of breakaway from both rear tires. If both tires leave marks, the axle is performing properly.

When you buy a new car, a limited-slip differential is normally an option. It's of greatest value if you do much of your driving in mud and/or snow—also on ice.

Whichever differential you have in your car, you can feel pretty good about it. There aren't many assemblies in your vehicle that need less maintenance. All that's involved for most is checking lubricant level whenever the chassis is lubricated.

To check level, remove the differential housing filler-hole plug and insert a clean finger in the filler hole to feel for the lubricant. If you feel the lube, reinsert and tighten the filler-hole plug. If lubricant is needed, add it using an inexpensive syringe.

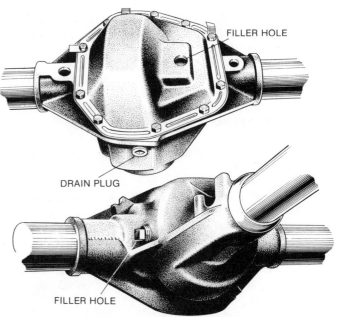

FILLER HOLE

DRAIN PLUG

FILLER HOLE

TEST MOST LIMITED-SLIP differentials by trying to rotate wheels (manual transmission in FIRST gear, automatic in PARK). If unit is okay, it should be very difficult or impossible to budge wheels.

BOTH FILLER HOLES and drain plugs are used on some differentials, as shown at top. Other differentials have only a filler hole, as shown above. When the differential has only a single filler hole, fill and drain it with a special suction tool.

Important: When checking lube level, make sure the car is level. In many cars, the filler-hole plug can be loosened and tightened with an ordinary open-end wrench. Other differentials are equipped with a recessed plug, requiring a special hex-type wrench to fit the recess.

If from one time to the next, the lube level drops appreciably, watch out. Low lubricant in a differential just doesn't happen. There has to be a reason, and that reason is usually a leak.

Look for a loose filler-hole plug, a leak between the housing and housing cover that indicates loose bolts or a ruptured gasket, or a crack in the housing itself. Loss of lube can also occur because of worn axle-shaft oil seals and a worn pinion shaft oil seal.

Most cars go a lifetime without having to have their differential drained. Others aren't so lucky.

If a differential is ever submerged in water and lubricant is even suspected of being contaminated, drain lubricant at once to prevent differential failure. Also, manufacturers generally recommend that differentials of cars used for towing trailers should have the lubricant drained periodically. Check maintenance instructions in your owner's or service manual.

There are two ways to drain a differential. Some units have drain holes as well as filler holes. Drive the car to get it warmed up. Then, remove the drain-hole plug and let lube pour out.

If your differential has a filler hole only, draining and filling is done with a special suction pump. Clean dirt from around the plug and remove it from the differential case. Draw out old lubricant through the filler plug hole by pulling it into the suction gun. After old lube has been removed, add fresh fluid through the filler plug hole by shooting it into the unit with the suction gun.

The kind of lube you use is important, especially if you have a limited-slip differential. Check manufacturer's recommendations.

If instructions don't call for a multiviscosity lube, keep in mind that viscosity-grade SAE 90 differential lube is generally used where the anticipated temperature will go no lower than minus 10° F. If the anticipated temperature is expected to go as low as minus 30° F., an SAE 80-grade lube will probably be prescribed.

Troubleshooting

If something happens to the differential in your car, chances are you're not going to be able to repair it yourself due to lack of experience, special equipment and facilities. But that doesn't mean you shouldn't familiarize yourself with the way differentials signify they're in trouble. Noise is the key.

Any time two gears mesh, there will be a certain amount of sound as the teeth come in contact. This should be a low-decibel sound no louder than normal driving noises from the engine, transmission and tires.

It's only when noise becomes loud that you should begin to worry. If caught early enough, differential noise often can be reduced by readjusting gears to mesh properly.

Try a road test

It is sometimes difficult to distinguish differential noise from other noises. The best way is with a road test, as follows:

1. Drive the car an appreciable distance. Noise coming from the differential is loudest when lube is warm.

2. Shut off all accessories.

3. Try to isolate the noise to a particular area. Differential noise is different than noises that come from engine and transmission. Tire noise is a continuous sound that varies with car speed. The sound changes pitch as tires encounter different road surfaces.

In comparison, differential noise is not affected by road surface changes. It tends to fade out below 30 mph. And it often changes pitch between driving and coasting conditions, while tire noise remains the same.

Another way to pinpoint bearing noise is to swerve the car sharply so body weight is shifted to the outside of the turn. Bad bearings will be louder when more pressure is put on them.

It's easy to distinguish automatic transmission noise from differential noise. Run the car under different transmission ranges. If changing the selector position causes the sound to occur at a higher or lower speed, you've isolated the noise to the transmission.

To single out engine or exhaust sounds, run the car and check the road speed at which the sound is most noticeable. Stop the car, put the transmission selector in N<small>EUTRAL</small> and again listen for the sound as you rev the engine to the approximate speed where the sound was heard. If you hear it again, the noise is coming either from the engine or exhaust.

Tree selection for your yard

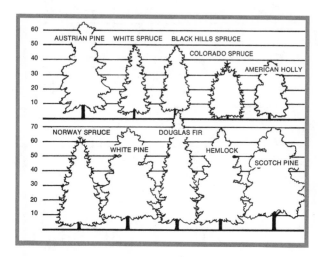

■ TREES ARE FOR COOLING SHADE in the summer, warming windbreak in the winter, fruit, blossoms, showy berries and colorful leaves. They are for climbing, building tree-houses in, swinging from.

Basic practicalities must be kept in mind. In a shade tree, for example, you want a species that grows well where you live, that leafs out early and holds leaves until late in the fall; that is deep-rooted so you can garden or grow grass beneath it; and that is resistant to pests and disease. Shade trees are undergoing major changes today, brought about by improved propagation techniques, widespread research to find varieties that are disease-resistant and pollution-tolerant.

Local climate is the first consideration in selecting a tree that will perform well over a long period of time. Trees native to the area are usually the very safest bet, if you don't mind limiting your selection.

Certain types of trees do better in an acid soil, others in alkaline ground (although minerals can be added to the soil to change its "sweetness").

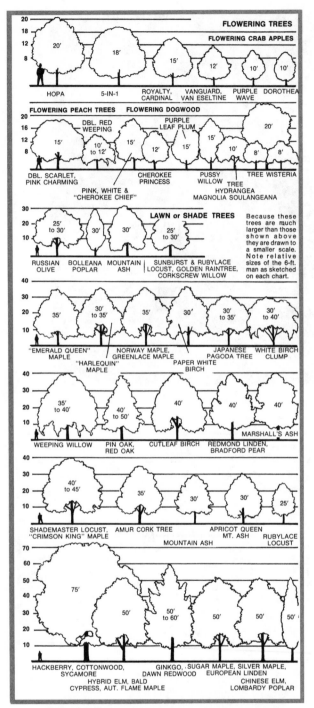

FLOWERING TREES

FLOWERING CRAB APPLES

20' 18 12 8 — 20' 18' 15' 12' 10' 10'

HOPA — 5-IN-1 — ROYALTY, CARDINAL — VANGUARD, VAN ESELTINE — PURPLE WAVE — DOROTHEA

FLOWERING PEACH TREES — **FLOWERING DOGWOOD**

20 16 12 8 — DBL. RED WEEPING — PURPLE LEAF PLUM — 20' — 15' — 10' to 12' — 15' — 12' — 15' — 15' — 10' — 8' — 8'

DBL. SCARLET, PINK CHARMING — CHEROKEE PRINCESS — PUSSY WILLOW — TREE WISTERIA
PINK, WHITE & "CHEROKEE CHIEF" — TREE HYDRANGEA — MAGNOLIA SOULANGEANA

LAWN or SHADE TREES

30 20 10 — 25' to 30' — 30' — 30' — 25' to 30'

Because these trees are much larger than those shown above they are drawn to a smaller scale. Note relative sizes of the 6-ft. man as sketched on each chart.

RUSSIAN OLIVE — BOLLEANA POPLAR — MOUNTAIN ASH — SUNBURST & RUBYLACE LOCUST, GOLDEN RAINTREE, CORKSCREW WILLOW

40 30 20 10 — 35' — 30' to 35' — 35' — 30' — 30' to 35' — 30' to 40'

"EMERALD QUEEN" MAPLE — NORWAY MAPLE, GREENLACE MAPLE — JAPANESE PAGODA TREE — WHITE BIRCH CLUMP
"HARLEQUIN" MAPLE — PAPER WHITE BIRCH

40 30 20 10 — 35' to 40' — 40' to 50' — 40' — 40' — 40'
MARSHALL'S ASH

WEEPING WILLOW — PIN OAK, RED OAK — CUTLEAF BIRCH — REDMOND LINDEN, BRADFORD PEAR

40 30 20 10 — 40' to 45' — 35' — 30' — 30' — 25'

SHADEMASTER LOCUST, "CRIMSON KING" MAPLE — AMUR CORK TREE — APRICOT QUEEN MT. ASH — RUBYLACE LOCUST
MOUNTAIN ASH

70 60 50 40 30 20 10 — 75' — 50' — 50' to 60' — 50' — 50' — 50'

HACKBERRY, COTTONWOOD, SYCAMORE — GINKGO, DAWN REDWOOD — SUGAR MAPLE, SILVER MAPLE, EUROPEAN LINDEN
HYBRID ELM, BALD CYPRESS, AUT. FLAME MAPLE — CHINESE ELM, LOMBARDY POPLAR

TREES ARE THE MOST important plantings you will make in your landscape. You plan for your own pleasure and that of future generations. Because of the long-range effects of planting a tree, consider its overall shape and expected size at maturity before you plant.

Some trees thrive in dry soil, others in wet. For specific recommendations about the most appropriate types for your area, check with your local nursery, arboretum, or the county office of your state Agricultural Extension Service.

Favorite shade tree recommendations by region include: *High Plains* (as in Colorado): thornless honey locust, green ash, Norway maple, hackberry, littleleaf linden. *Midwest* (as in Minnesota): sugar maple, Norway maple, green ash, Crimean linden, white oak. *Southeast* (as in Georgia): evergreen live oak or willow oak, American holly, magnolia grandiflora, dogwood, loquat. *North Central/East* (as in Ohio): Norway maple, sugar maple, red maple, littleleaf linden, pin oak. *Desert* (as in New Mexico): Arizona ash, pecan, thornless honey locust, fruitless mulberry, Aleppo pine. *Southern California* (as in Los Angeles): fruitless mulberry, fern pine, magnolia grandiflora, Koelreuteria integrifoliola, Brazilian pepper.

Flowering trees stay small, give a burst of bloom in season and all are useful for light shade. They fit well into a small lot, especially at corners, make an excellent privacy screen if planted closely along the edge of the yard, and look well placed three or more in a clump to achieve a full, natural effect. Favorites include redbud, crab apple, English hawthorn, European mountain ash, flowering cherry, peach and plum, dogwood, franklinia, fringe tree, golden chain.

Evergreens provide shade all year and are outstanding as a winter windbreak. Kinds that mature at 30 feet or larger include American arborvitae and holly, Austrian pine, Black Hills spruce, Cedar of Lebanon, Colorado spruce, Douglas fir, Eastern hemlock, Norway pine.

Almost any variety of tree has some disadvantage that must be weighed against its good points. Thus, it's not a good idea to choose elms, willows, poplars or maples for planting near drainage pipes, because the roots of these trees can clog sewers. Species with shallow roots rob lawns of moisture and if planted near a sidewalk can break the pavement.

Some trees are extremely susceptible to insects or disease. A notable example is the American elm, favorite street tree of U.S. cities until it was decimated by Dutch Elm disease.

Fell and limb a tree

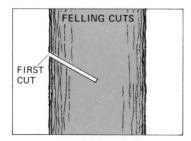
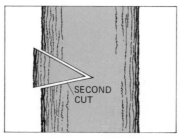
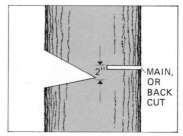

■ DONE PROPERLY, it takes three cuts to fell a tree: two passes to make the undercut (notch) and a back cut on the opposite side of the trunk. If you are a beginner, mark all three cuts waist high on the tree trunk with chalk. The notch should be cut in the sequence shown above to a depth of approximately one-third tree diameter, and perpendicular to the line of fall. After making the first two cuts, remove the wedge from the trunk.

Make the back cut at least 2 in. higher than the notch so as to leave a "hinge" of uncut wood to guide the tree over. *Do not cut through the notch.* Besides guiding the tree, the hinge will also prevent the tree from twisting as it falls. As the tree starts to fall, pull your saw free. Immediately turn off power and retreat quickly along your preplanned escape route. From here on, gravity takes over.

Sawing sequence for large-diameter trunks

As a rule of thumb, large-diameter trees (up to twice the chain-saw-bar length in diameter)

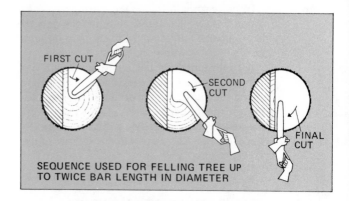

SEQUENCE USED FOR FELLING TREE UP TO TWICE BAR LENGTH IN DIAMETER

should be handled by a professional; cutting one down is not a job for a fledgling woodcutter. However, if you are confident of your tree-felling ability, and the tree is standing out in open terrain, you should always use felling wedges in the manner described above.

To fell a large tree, use a series of cuts as shown. Notice that the cuts are made so that the third and final cut leaves the hinge wood parallel to the notch cut. This is a must, so make the cuts with maximum care.

When to use a felling wedge

If you suspect the tree may not fall in the desired direction, or may tilt back causing the saw to bind, do not complete the back cut. Withdraw the saw and use wood, plastic or magnesium wedges to open the cut and tilt the tree in the desired direction of fall. *Caution: When using wedges, make certain the chain saw does not come into contact with wedge or the saw will kick back.* Felling wedges are available at most chain-saw dealers or you can cut your own hardwood.

With the tree felled, you can now trim off the waist-high stump close to the ground, repeating the three-cut method mentioned above.

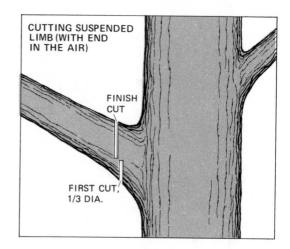

FELLING WEDGE

Limbing a tree

There are two things to guard against when limbing a tree: first, the possibility that the cut branch will whip back in the direction of the woodcutter; and second, the impulse to work from an improperly positioned, thus unsafe, ladder.

To prevent the first, use the cutting sequence shown. To saw off a large limb supported only by the trunk, first cut one-third of the way through the limb on its underside. Make second cut through the limb from the top. Make certain you lash the ladder securely to the tree. Run a rope around the trunk a couple of times, then tie it securely to the top rung. Plant the ladder so that its feet are level and are placed a distance from the base of the tree that is equal to one-quarter of the vertical height.

CUTTING SUSPENDED LIMB (WITH END IN THE AIR)

FINISH CUT

FIRST CUT, 1/3 DIA.

LOGS CUT AND SPLIT, THEN STACKED TO PROVIDE AIR CIRCULATION

Stacking fireplace logs

For use as firewood, the logs should be stacked and allowed to dry. There is a difference of opinion on whether to split logs before or after they are dry. Splitting goes quickest if you use a steel splitting wedge and a wooden maul rather than an ax. And it's a lot safer.

Twelve or fourteen logs may be stored without danger of toppling over. One cord of wood equals 128 cu. ft. Assuming you've cut your logs into 24-in. lengths, it would take a pile 16 ft. long and 4 ft. high to equal this volume.

Avoiding kickback

When cutting with the nose of the bar, take extra care to protect against saw kickback. It will occur when any of the three conditions illustrated exists.

Safety rules you should always observe.

1. Think the job out beforehand and stick to your plan.

2. Plan an escape route at 45° angle opposite the direction of tree fall.

3. Wear a hard hat if there is any chance of timber or branches falling from above.

4. Don't wear loose-fitting clothing. It could become caught in the chain saw or falling limbs. Always wear work gloves.

5. If your job collects a crowd, stop. Keep by-standers, especially children, clear of your cutting site and area of tree fall.

6. Work only with a sharp saw chain.

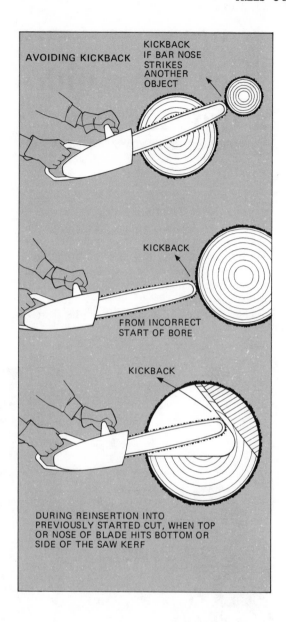

AVOIDING KICKBACK   KICKBACK IF BAR NOSE STRIKES ANOTHER OBJECT

KICKBACK FROM INCORRECT START OF BORE

KICKBACK

DURING REINSERTION INTO PREVIOUSLY STARTED CUT, WHEN TOP OR NOSE OF BLADE HITS BOTTOM OR SIDE OF THE SAW KERF

Fell a tree with a two-man saw

■ ONE- AND TWO-MAN crosscut saws will never replace the chain saw for many people. For some, however, it provides a sensible alternative. The trick is to spread out your woodcutting chore over two or three dozen hour-long stints—instead of two or three all-day marathon sessions with a chain saw.

There are several bonuses, not the least of which is that it's more healthful. In an age of paying money to keep in shape, a crosscut saw is a cheap and productive way to get exercise. The saw shouldn't cost you much more than a couple of hours of tennis-court time, or the price of new running shoes. It won't numb your arms or ears with intense vibrations and noise, the way prolonged use of a chain saw will.

The crosscut saw is cheaper and less messy. There's no worry about mixing gasoline and oil. And it will always "start."

If you want to buy a saw, here are some pointers:

● Two types of basic blades are available—one-man and two-man crosscut saws.

● A one-man saw is asymmetrical and features a conventional saw handle at the wide end of the blade. An auxiliary handle can be attached to the small end of the blade to allow two people to work the saw. One-man saws, once produced in

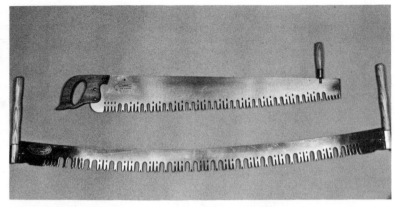

CROSSCUT SAWS are available in one- and two-man types. With the addition of an auxiliary handle (above), two men can work a one-man saw.

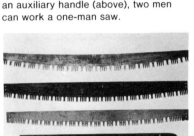

SAW PATTERNS vary but fall into two classes: felling and bucking. Felling has curved back, bucking straight.

OLD-STYLE SAW handles, often seen at flea markets, have rugged guards to prevent jammed fingers.

ANOTHER desirable feature is adjustable handles that let the grip rotate 90°— handy for avoiding obstacles.

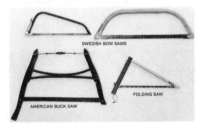

SMALL-SIZE crosscut saws (above), which are handy for the cutting of small-diameter logs, are equipped with replaceable blades. The folding types are especially handy for backpackers (below).

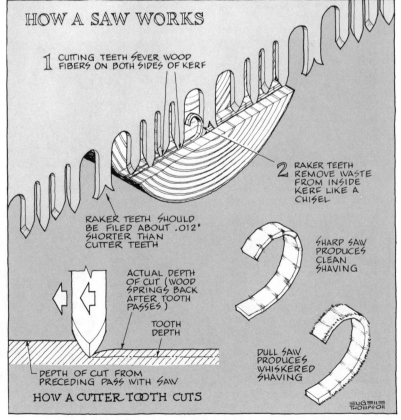

HOW A SAW WORKS

1 CUTTING TEETH SEVER WOOD FIBERS ON BOTH SIDES OF KERF

2 RAKER TEETH REMOVE WASTE FROM INSIDE KERF LIKE A CHISEL

RAKER TEETH SHOULD BE FILED ABOUT .012" SHORTER THAN CUTTER TEETH

SHARP SAW PRODUCES CLEAN SHAVING

ACTUAL DEPTH OF CUT (WOOD SPRINGS BACK AFTER TOOTH PASSES)

TOOTH DEPTH

DULL SAW PRODUCES WHISKERED SHAVING

DEPTH OF CUT FROM PRECEDING PASS WITH SAW

HOW A CUTTER TOOTH CUTS

lengths from 3 to 6 ft., are available today in 3-, 3½- and 4½-ft. lengths.

● Two-man saws are symmetrical and have a handle at each end. Two types exist—the felling saw for dropping timber and the bucksaw for cutting the dropped tree into shorter lengths. A felling saw has a narrower blade and a concave back. It is lighter than a bucksaw and more flexible. Bucksaws come with a straight back and are thicker, stiffer and heavier than felling saws. The weight is desirable, since it helps the teeth bite deeper and speeds cutting. Stiffness allows the saw to be run by one person.

While many felling saws and bucksaws are still around, some modern blades have characteristics of both types and could be called utility saws. They work well on many jobs.

Handsaws are least expensive at secondhand stores, garage sales, surplus stores and flea markets.

Avoid saws with pitted and rusty blades. Check a blade carefully—look for broken teeth, kinks or other signs that it has been roughly treated. If possible, look at several different saws before you buy, so you can recognize basic characteristics.

HOW TO FELL A TREE WITH A TWO-MAN SAW

Here are tips for anyone gung-ho enough to want to fell a tree with a crosscut saw.

1. If you've bought a new saw, don't assume it's ready to use. A factory grinding wheel used to sharpen the teeth often leaves burrs that need smoothing with a crosscut file.

2. Know the type wood (hard, soft, green, punky and so on) you'll be cutting so you can prepare your saw properly at home.

3. If you have no experience in judging which is the best direction to fell a tree, bring along someone who does.

4. Besides the saw, bring a hatchet for clearing underbrush from the working area, kerosene for lubricating the blade, an ax for completing felling notches, work gloves and a file and setting device in case teeth should need touching up. Finally, if possible, bring a sawbuck for cutting logs into manageable lengths.

TO DROP a tree, cut notch in direction of fall. Undercut ⅓ diameter of tree and chop out a 30° notch.

BACK CUT (opposite notch) is made 1 to 2 in. above undercut level. Leave 2-in. portion (hinge) uncut.

PRIOR TO making either cut, chip away bark with a hatchet. Dirt and bark may dull saw quickly.

IF SAW BINDS, drive wedges as needed to free blade and continue sawing.

BE CERTAIN escape path is clear of obstacles *before* you start. Best angles of departure are 45° from fall.

ONCE TREE is on the ground, use sawbuck and one- or two-man bucksaw to cut log into desired lengths.

SAW-SETTING TOOL adjusts to set cutter teeth by repositioning a machine screw.

FILING CUTTER and raker teeth is best accomplished with blade securely clamped in pivoting saw vise.

A BLADE GUARD for carrying your saw can be made from old fire hose or canvas.

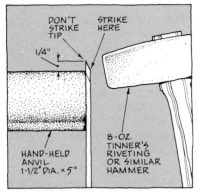

EXPERTS recommend using a hammer with a small strike face, anvil and spider gauge to set the teeth.

IDEAL KIT for sharpening and setting: 8-oz. tinner's hammer (A), anvil (B), spider gauge (C), jointer and raker combination depth gauge (D) and files (E).

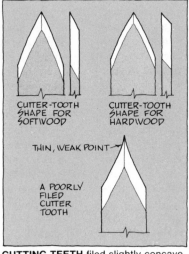

CUTTING TEETH filed slightly concave are easier to pull through wood. Use proper shape for wood type.

CARRY SAW on downhill shoulder with rear handle removed and teeth pointed away from neck. Walk last in line.

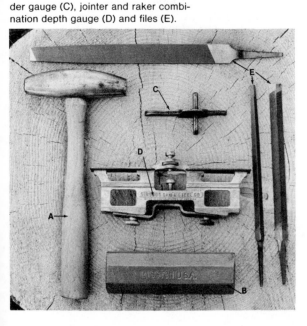

On many crosscut saws, a common tooth pattern features four cutter teeth to each raker tooth. The tooth lengths vary between brands; excessively short teeth may indicate the blade has been filed many times and is almost worn out.

Handling a crosscut saw

While crosscut saws are safer than chain saws, several items should be remembered when using the blades. First, make a blade guard. A piece of fire hose or heavy canvas and large rubber bands cut from old inner tubes work nicely. Keep the blade covered until you reach the work site.

In a vehicle, remove the guard and sandwich the blade between two plywood strips. This keeps the teeth from punching through the hose and dulling against metal. Bolts and wingnuts secure the package.

Before you begin sawing, clear the area around the cutting site so the saw won't hang up on limbs or underbrush. Remove any bark at the point of cutting. Bark often contains dirt and grit that will dull teeth or jam the blade in the cut.

Evaluate potential safety problems before you start. Will a log shift or roll once you cut it through? Will a bent tree spring loose, once some weight is cut free? Are you on a hill? Cutting standing timber is particularly hazardous and should only be attempted in the company of an experienced woodsman.

Once the cut is started, remember the word "pull." If the saw is in good order, simply concentrate on pulling the blade toward you—your partner will pull it back. Pushing a saw may bend the blade and cause it to hang up in the cut, destroying the rhythm of your strokes. Once you achieve a consistent harmony with your partner, you may wish to experiment by adding some muscle on the push strokes.

The position of your hands on the handles affects the ease or difficulty you may have in sawing. A pull stroke is easier if the handle is in the "up" position and held near the end. Some saws have two mounting holes for each handle, allowing more adjustment to help you achieve the most efficient position.

If the wood you're cutting is green, sap may stick to the blade and cause it to jam. Lubricate the blade with kerosene when it begins to feel sticky.

Sharpening and setting

If most of your cutting is in one place, a good sawbuck is worth building. It helps keep the blade out of the dirt, lets the cut open without wedging and permits a more comfortable stance for the sawyer.

One way to get your saw sharp is to have a professional do it, but if the classified pages don't turn up a sharpener (they're a disappearing breed), the alternative is to do it yourself. First, buy a copy of the *Crosscut Saw Manual* by Warren Miller for full information on crosscut-saw reconditioning, filing, maintenance and use. It also has a plan for building a sharpening vise. You can get this book from the Superintendent of Documents, U.S. Government Printing Office, Washington, DC 20402.

Next, gather the sharpening aids which will make your task easier. Here's what you'll need:

A jointer-raker combination gauge for filing the cutting teeth to conform to the arc of the blade and for setting the depth of the raker teeth. A .008-in. depth is desirable for hard or dry wood and .030 in. is recommended for soft or springy wood. A good average starting figure is .012.

A setting tool or anvil and hammer for setting the end of the cutter teeth. Set varies depending on the saw and the wood being cut. Generally, the harder the wood, the less the set—to a minimum of .010 in. Soft, punky or green wood requires a greater set, .030 in. or more for some saws. A little experimentation is required. The small gauges which are known as spiders make accurate setting easier.

A 7- or 8-in. crosscut file and saw vise for sharpening. Attempt to maintain the cutter-tooth bevel supplied on the saw.

Unfortunately, makers of jointing and raker depth-setting tools are no longer around. Jointing is often done with a long file and raker-depth setting is also improvised, using a gauge for gapping sparkplugs.

Small-size crosscut saws

If you are not quite ready for a crosscut saw, but still need a saw for lighter-duty tasks, one of the following may serve your needs:

The traditional American bucksaw, always found near Grandfather's woodpile, features a 30-in. blade and a hardwood frame.

The Swedish bow saw has a tubular-steel frame and comes in various sizes and tooth patterns. Mostly, these have replaced the bucksaw in today's hardware stores.

The Sven saw, a lightweight bow type, has a 20-in. blade which folds into the handle when not in use.

Metal tubing: look what you can make

■ MANY USEFUL OBJECTS can be made from aluminum, copper, brass or steel tubing. Metal tubing is cut with a hacksaw, tubing cutter or lathe. Cut ends are file-finished, or smoothed in a lathe. For smooth surfaces, abrasive cloth or a flap-type sanding wheel is used and a final luster is given with metal polish. Tubing can be joined by soldering, brazing, welding—or even using epoxy or plugs (either metal or wood) and

SOME METAL TUBING can be bent satisfactorily simply by wrapping it around grooved pulley wheel (sheave). Here, ⅜-in. aluminum tubing is bent this way.

VARIOUS ITEMS that can be made from metal tubing include: ring basket or tray; siphon; shelf bracket; drawer or door pull; slide whistle; metal tubing with ends flattened, connected by peened spacers; adjustable shelf post/bookend; spacer; brush handle; file handle.

screws, pins or nails. Bending can be done with coil-spring sleeves or the method shown in the photo.

Details on six metal tubing projects follow. All sizes of tubing given refer to outside dimensions.

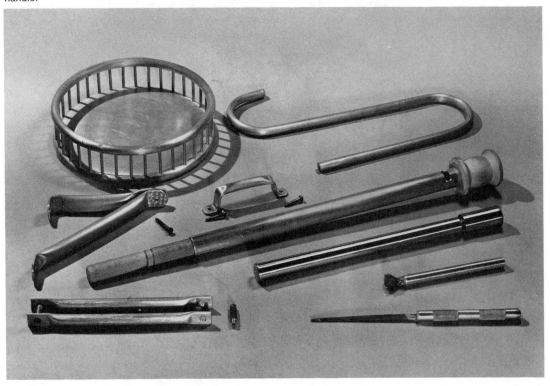

SPACER with the diameter of the ends reduced connects the flattened ends of the larger tubing. Here, the spacer ends are peened to hold ends together.

ALUMINUM TUBING can be closed and rounded by first cutting it as shown. Then, use a hammer to lightly tap the cut ends until it is round.

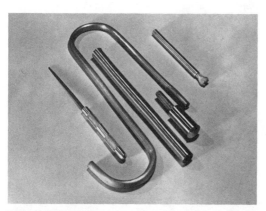

TOOL HANDLES and siphon made from ⅜-in. aluminum tube; post bookend from ¾ and ⅝-in. copper tubes.

ADJUSTABLE BOOKSHELF POST serves as a bookend and as an added support for the upper shelf.

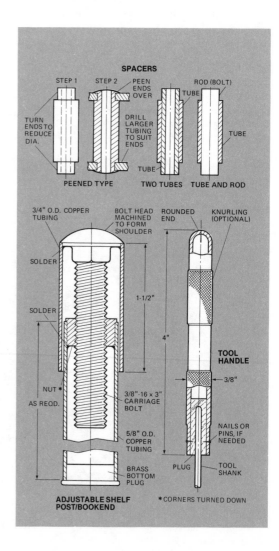

Spacers

Short lengths of tubing are often used as spacers between two plates, strips or other elements of a mechanism. One type of spacer is made from a single tube, with the ends turned or filed down to form shoulders and peened over after installation. A tube, rod or bolt within a tube might also be used.

Tool handles

Improvised tool handles can be made easily from tubing. A common way to anchor the tool shank is to drive a wood dowel into the tube and drill a hole in the dowel for the tool. The relatively new "plastic-metal" preparations or an epoxy filler could also be used. Outer end of the handle can be left open, plugged or closed by using the method shown or by spinning or bending the metal. Light knurling makes a handle less slippery.

Adjustable shelf post/bookend

This dual-purpose item is made from ⅝ and ¾-in. copper tubing with a ⅜-16 x 3-in. carriage bolt and nut providing the adjustable movement. Nut corners are turned down for about ⅚ of their length, forming a shoulder to rest on end of ⅝-in. tubing (see drawing). The bolt head is machined to form a shallow shoulder to rest on the end of ¾-in. tubing. Nut and bolt head are soldered to their respective tubes by fluxing the joints, placing bits of solder inside the tubes and heating over stove burner. Plug at bottom of post prevents denting the shelf.

Shelf bracket

By flattening ends of two lengths of aluminum tubing and drilling screw holes in them, a handy shelf bracket can be made.

SHELF BRACKET is made from ½-in. aluminum tubing; whistle from ¾-in. aluminum tubing, dowel and spool.

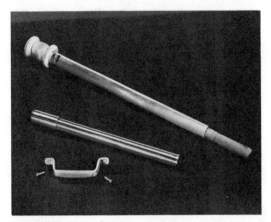

FROM TOP: assembled slide whistle, adjustable bookshelf post, drawer pull from ⅜-in. aluminum tubing.

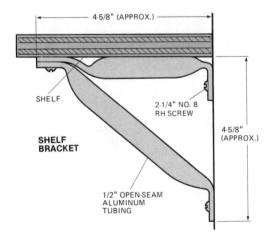

SHELF BRACKET

4-5/8" (APPROX.)

SHELF

2-1/4" NO. 8 RH SCREW

4-5/8" (APPROX.)

1/2" OPEN-SEAM ALUMINUM TUBING

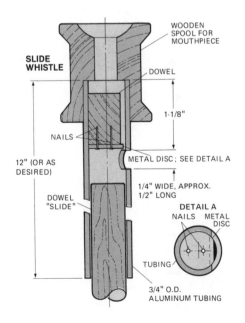

SLIDE WHISTLE

WOODEN SPOOL FOR MOUTHPIECE

DOWEL

1-1/8"

NAILS

METAL DISC; SEE DETAIL A

12" (OR AS DESIRED)

1/4" WIDE, APPROX. 1/2" LONG

DOWEL "SLIDE"

DETAIL A

NAILS   METAL DISC

TUBING

3/4" O.D. ALUMINUM TUBING

NAILS IN clamped wood hold metal ring in place for drilling holes in center of rim to receive "side rods."

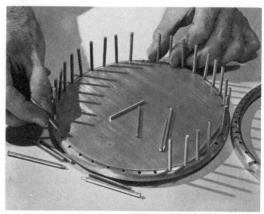

"**SIDE RODS**" (nails with heads cut off) are inserted in bottom ring holes; sheet aluminum bottom fits inside.

BASKET made from ⅜-in. seamless aluminum tubing and aluminum nails makes attractive server.

Slide whistle

A slot in the tube is made by drilling two ¼-in. holes tangential to one another and filing out intervening metal. The plug is a short piece of dowel; a metal disc with a flat area on its circumference is nailed to one end of the plug and positioned at slot edge. The slide is a free-moving length of dowel, the mouthpiece, a wood spool.

Ring basket

Two lengths of metal tubing are bent to form two circles with 7-in. outside diameters. Ends of each circle are joined by inserting a maple plug and nailing through tubing into plug. The circles are joined with 36 "side rods" made by cutting heads from ⅛-in.-dia. aluminum nails. A total of 33 "rods" engage holes drilled through one side of each ring; the other three are longer and extend through rings with their ends peened. The bottom piece is sheet aluminum cut from siding scrap and glued in place with epoxy cement.

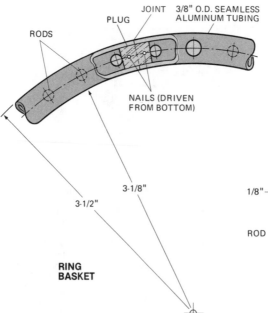

RODS

PLUG

JOINT   3/8" O.D. SEAMLESS
        ALUMINUM TUBING

NAILS (DRIVEN
FROM BOTTOM)

3-1/8"

3-1/2"

**RING
BASKET**

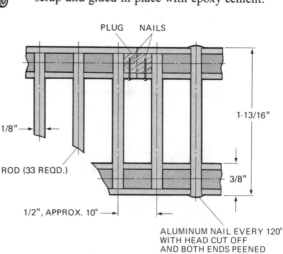

PLUG   NAILS

1-13/16"

1/8"

3/8"

ROD (33 REQD.)

1/2", APPROX. 10°

ALUMINUM NAIL EVERY 120°
WITH HEAD CUT OFF
AND BOTH ENDS PEENED

BLOCK SPACERS are cut from 2x4 stock. Spacers are laid out, corner holes for conduit drilled before spacers are cut to shape.

Thinwall conduit makes rugged masts

■ WHETHER USED to support a TV antenna or a 10-room martin birdhouse, a high-rise mast can weigh and cost like the dickens. But you can assemble a sturdy lightweight one for a few dollars from standard lengths of thinwall conduit.

You have a choice of bracing the three-legged masts with a series of thinwall spacers (A) flattened at the ends, or with wood blocks placed every 12 in. The wood blocks (B) are attached with 1½-in. No. 10 screws; the thinwall sections are brazed. A three-hole wood fixture keeps conduit legs uniformly spaced while being brazed.

If the mast is to support a birdhouse, it's anchored to long bolts imbedded in a concrete footing, and metal angles are used at the top to attach the birdhouse. If used to mount a TV antenna on the roof, the legs of the mast are bolted to three angle-iron feet. In the case of a TV mast, the upper ends of the three legs can be ''gathered'' around an additional single length of conduit and cross-bolted together. In some cases, you may need to brace the mast with guy wires.

CONDUIT LEGS and wooden spacers are joined with screws. To avoid stains from rust, be sure to use galvanized screws.

ANCHOR BOLTS, two 5/8-in. and one 1/2-in., are set in concrete to project 3 to 5 in. The smaller bolt makes up for misalignment.

HIGH-RISE MAST is slipped over the anchor bolts and then cross-pinned with three 1/4-in. bolts. Use washers under legs, if needed, to level legs.

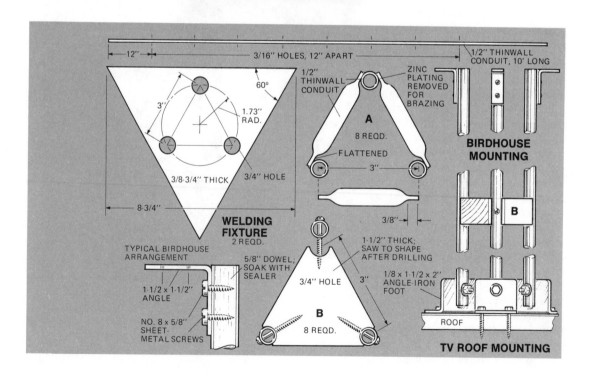

12″

3/16″ HOLES, 12″ APART

1/2″ THINWALL CONDUIT, 10′ LONG

60°

3″

1.73″ RAD.

1/2″ THINWALL CONDUIT

ZINC PLATING REMOVED FOR BRAZING

A

8 REQD.

FLATTENED

3″

3/8-3/4″ THICK

3/4″ HOLE

8-3/4″

WELDING FIXTURE
2 REQD.

3/8″

BIRDHOUSE MOUNTING

B

TYPICAL BIRDHOUSE ARRANGEMENT

5/8″ DOWEL; SOAK WITH SEALER

1-1/2″ THICK; SAW TO SHAPE AFTER DRILLING

1/8 x 1-1/2 x 2″ ANGLE-IRON FOOT

1-1/2 x 1-1/2″ ANGLE

3/4″ HOLE

3″

NO. 8 x 5/8″ SHEET-METAL SCREWS

B

8 REQD.

ROOF

TV ROOF MOUNTING

Upholstery basic course

■ YOU CAN SAVE MONEY by reupholstering your own sofa or chair. Substantial savings are good reasons why you should find out how to do your own upholstery work. It is one kind of do-it-yourself activity that truly pays for itself.

To begin with, most reupholstery work is simple and straightforward, so it is easy to learn. You don't need many tools, and the ones you do need are not expensive. And tools and materials are readily available all over the country in upholstery and fabric shops.

The best way to learn to reupholster is to find an old chair or two and practice on them. Look for chairs that are simple in design—ones without special pleating, unusual shapes or obviously complicated covering jobs. Later, you'll be able to do work like this, but for your first try, practice on jobs that aren't complex. Buy some inexpensive cover fabric and rework these chairs from the frame out. By the time you have finished them, you'll have gained both experience and confidence. Then you'll be ready to work with more expensive fabrics and be able to do a creditable job on your good furniture. You'll work your way out of your mistakes—and you'll end up with a couple of useful chairs.

The tools needed are few and inexpensive. You can buy a kit at most fabric and upholstery stores. It contains a magnetic tack hammer, a tack lifter, a webbing stretcher and several large sewing needles. Add to this a couple of screwdrivers and a pair of pliers and you have everything you need.

Recently, a lot of upholstery work has been done with staples instead of tacks. Staples offend the traditionalists, who feel that they cheapen the work, but staples are effective in 90 percent of the work—and in some cases are better than tacks. For example, staples are less likely to split the wood, especially when you drive them near the edge of a seat rail.

THE FIRST STEP in any reupholstery job is to take off the old fabric. Here a tack lifter and hammer are used to remove the tacks holding the dust cover on a sofa. Using the hammer with the lifter speeds the work.

The trick in using staples is to use staples that are long enough. Also, use a gun which has enough power to drive the staples completely into the wood. The ideal tool, when you use staples, is an electric staple gun. These are a good investment if you intend to do much upholstery work. Buy a gun which can drive staples of different lengths (most will) because you need to be able to choose the size of the staple. When putting on a cambric dust cover, for example, you need a very short staple. But when you must tack through several layers of fabric, you need a staple with legs ½ in. long or more.

You also can staple with a hand gun. The gun should be able to drive staples of different lengths, too, and should be powerful enough to drive them all the way into the wood. Most furniture frames are made of hardwood, which resists staples, and a gun which isn't powerful enough will not drive long staples all the way.

The electric gun is particularly good when you upholster a couch, where you must drive hundreds of staples. With a hand gun, your hand will be aching by the time you finish. With an electric gun, you can do the work quickly and without fatigue.

Upholstering materials—tools, fabric, and padding are easy to find. Most professional upholstery shops will sell you what you need, and fabric shops today carry a full line of upholstery goods.

In many cases, you'll find you can reuse the padding from the piece you are redoing. You can also reuse the springs. You'll need new webbing, perhaps some new padding and, of course, new fabric for the final cover.

Keep in mind that your first chair is your best textbook in upholstering. Strip the old upholstery from it slowly and with care. Study the chair as you work, noting how the fabric was applied, how the corners were made, where the upholsterer used a needle and thread and where he used tacks. Don't just rip the old cover off, even if it is badly worn, but remove it carefully, a piece at a time. Save each piece of fabric and padding, because these can serve as patterns when you cut and shape the new materials.

Pay special attention to the way the fabric is folded, pleated or tucked at the corners, since corners usually prove to be the biggest mystery for the beginner. If necessary, make notes and

CORNERS ON UPHOLSTERY work should be firm and square. As you apply the final fabric, use wads of cotton or polyester to shape them.

sketches for later reference. Watch to see how the material was cut to fit around posts, keeping in mind that when you apply the new cover, you'll want to cut the fabric the same way.

One final equipment note: It is very helpful to have a sewing machine available when you up-

TO FIT THE FABRIC around leg and arm posts, you must make cuts. Here the fabric is cut to fit around the back posts of a sofa.

A LONG, SMOOTH STICK serves as a stuffer to help push the fabric through the slot between the sofa back and seat. Fabric is tacked at the back.

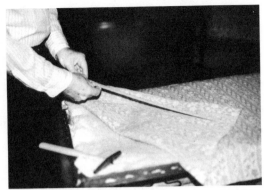

A TACKING STRIP with the tacks already embedded in it is handy for making closures. You can buy these strips by the foot at fabric stores.

THE TACKING STRIP is placed in the folded end of the material, with the tacks pointing down toward the frame. Push the tacks through the material.

USING PLIERS to pull the fabric tight, you then drive the tacks into the frame. The tacks are invisible and the result is a neat blind tacking job.

holster. Almost every upholstering job requires welting or cording, which you must make from the fabric you intend to use as a final cover. Hand sewing of welting can be a long and tedious job. You'll also want a sewing machine for joining pieces of the cover and for sewing stretch

ELECTRIC STAPLE DRIVER is a very handy tool for upholstery work. Look for one which will drive staples of different lengths.

tabs of old fabric to your new cover material. This latter gimmick cuts down on the amount of expensive fabric you need, since in using it, you use an old fabric as a pull tab and use the good fabric only in the places where it shows.

Materials

Here is some information on the upholstery materials you will need:

Tacks. Upholstery tacks are the standard tacks with which you already are familiar. They come in sizes identified by numbers. No. 1 (1 oz.) tacks are small, used to tack the dust cover on the bottom of furniture. Nos. 3 and 4 are all-purpose tacks, used for tacking on muslin covers, final fabric, and burlap. Most of your work is done with these sizes. No. 6 tacks are larger, used for tacking through folded material and very heavy materials. Nos. 12 and 14 tacks are jumbo-size, for tacking down jute webbing, anchoring seat twine, etc. If you intend to use tacks in your work, buy boxes of these sizes, with emphasis on Nos. 3 and 4.

Webbing. Furniture webbing is made of jute and is used to support the coil springs. It usually is available in a 3½-in. width. You'll use 10 to 12 yds. on a typical chair, and 30 yards or so to do a sofa.

Rubber webbing is used in some chairs (Danish types, for example), but since it deteriorates rapidly, you should think about replacing it with jute webbing. Your final decision may be influenced by the design of the furniture. Chairs with rubber webbing frequently are designed without springs, and depend on the spring of the rubber for comfort.

THE FIRST STEP in installing new webbing is to lay the webbing on the bottom of the frame and anchor it with four tacks.

NEXT, FOLD the end of the webbing back across the first tacks and drive three more. Magnetic tack hammer makes driving tacks easy.

USING A webbing stretcher, pull the webbing tight across the frame. As you hold it, drive four tacks, then cut webbing 1½ in. from frame.

Springs. There are two basic types of springs used in furniture, the coil and the zig-zag. Unless the springs in your furniture have somehow been broken, there is no need to replace them. Coil springs need to be retied, and zig-zags may need to be reanchored in the chair frame. If you should have to replace a spring, take the broken spring to an upholstery shop. The proprietor can give a replacement of the correct size and tension.

When zig-zag springs come loose from the frame, they must be repositioned by stretching them across the seat opening and renailing them to the frame.

Thread and twine. Use a heavy flax or linen thread for all upholstery work. The thread called *carpet thread* is fine for this work. Use it in conjunction with large sailor's needles, both straight and curved. Twine is used for tying the springs, and the best twine, which has the necessary strength and is slow to deteriorate, is 6-ply hemp, which can be purchased in large balls. Ordinary cotton twine and most packaging twines either break too easily or deteriorate too quickly.

Burlap. Burlap is used to cover the springs after they have been tied, and to cover layers of padding. As a rule, the 12-oz. material is best for most upholstery work.

Stuffing. Three basic types of stuffing or padding are used in upholstery work: fiber, felt and foam.

The fiber stuffings include curled animal hair (the finest); Spanish moss (next best); and excelsior (poorest and cheapest). Usually you can buy sheets of rubberized hair at fabric shops, and may find that this is best to use.

Felt stuffings include cotton, kapok and those consisting of polyester fibers, all of which come in pads. Kapok is the least desirable because it tends to separate into lumps. Cotton is the old standby. But at present, the most available padding is polyester, which is softer and lighter than cotton. It doesn't pack down and it doesn't deteriorate. It is easy to use.

A lot of furniture is now padded with foam. The older work was done with foam rubber, but today, much better polyurethane foam has taken over. You can buy this in sheets of different thicknesses, and in preformed cushions and pillows. You can cut this foam easily, and can make pads of different shapes by cementing the pieces together. If you are replacing an old foam padding, simply make new padding pieces the size and shape of the old ones. If you have decided to replace cotton or other padding with foam, use a

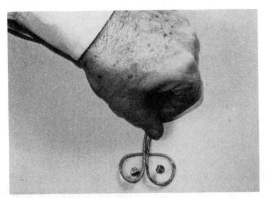

WHEN TYING SPRINGS, the tying twine is anchored to the sides of the chair or sofa rails by means of two No. 12 tacks. After looping, drive tacks in.

SPRINGS ARE TIED from front to back, then from side to side. Knot is made at each point where the twine crosses a coil. Use strong 6-ply hemp twine.

SEAT IS SHAPED as you tie the springs. Here, diagonal ties complete the shaping. Springs near the seat rail are compressed to round the seat.

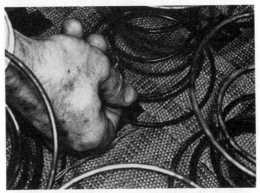

AFTER REPLACEMENT, sew springs to the webbing. Each spring is ''tacked'' to the webbing in four places. Thread is heavyweight carpet type.

sharp knife or scissors to shape the foam pieces to fit the chair.

Edge rolls. An edge roll is a type of padding used around the edge of seats and chair backs to both pad and shape the outer contours of the furniture. You can buy them ready-made, or make them yourself by wrapping burlap around rolls of hair, cotton, or polyester. The final edge roll looks like a long sausage from ½ to 1½ in. in diameter, with a tab along one side to be used for tacking it in position. You can save any edge rolls you find on furniture as you strip it, and reuse them during reupholstery.

Tacking strips. A tacking strip is a long strip of cardboard ½ in. wide. You can buy it by the yard or in rolls. It is used in blind tacking, as shown in the photographs. You can also buy tacking strips with large tacks already inserted in the cardboard. These are used in making final closures—as when you tack down the cover fabric on the back of a sofa.

Cambric. Thin black cambric is tacked to the bottom of every upholstered piece to serve as a dust cover.

Welting. Welting is used in most chairs and sofas at those points where fabric pieces meet, to provide a finished look. Welting is made from the fabric you are using as a final cover. You do this by cutting strips of the fabric 2 in. wide and then sewing these strips around welting cord.

Measure the running feet of welting you need for your work, then cut enough strips of fabric 2 in. wide to make this much. You may need 15 to 20 feet for a chair, and three times that amount for a sofa. Begin by sewing all the 2-in strips of fabric you have cut end to end, making one long strip 2 in. wide. Trim any excess fabric from each sewn seam to prevent bulges in the welting. Now wrap the 2-in. strip around the welting cord (which can be purchased at fabric shops) and use the sewing machine to stitch through both layers of fabric right next to the wrapped cord. The finished piece of welting has the fabric wrapped tightly around the welting cord, and two flaps about ¾ in. long for tacking.

Stripping the old upholstery. The best tools for this job are a light hammer and a tack lifter. The easiest way to remove a tack is to place the blades of the tack lifter next to the tack head, and then gently tap the handle of the lifter with the hammer, guiding the blades under the tack head as you tap. The head will lift after several taps.

The first fabric to strip off is the cambric dust cover on the bottom. Turn the chair or sofa over, supporting it on a sawhorse while you work. Lift out the tacks holding the dust cover in place. While the piece is upside down, you can also remove the tacks which secure the final fabric of the seat and back which are tacked to the bottom side of the bottom rails.

Now turn the piece right side up and take off the outside back cover. If this piece has been sewn to the side fabric pieces, cut the thread to remove it—and at the same time, make a note to yourself to sew the new cover on in the same manner.

Now take off the outside arm covers. Observe carefully how these pieces have been attached to the front of the arm, and how the fabric has been cut to fit around the leg and back posts. You may find that the top of the outside arm fabric has been blind tacked, using a tacking strip. Make a note of this.

Now remove the inside back cover, starting by pulling the fabric up through the bottom frame since you have already removed the tacks holding this piece to the bottom rail. Be sure to save each of the old cover pieces to serve as a later reference. Also, as you take off each cover piece lift out the padding under it. Some of this padding may be tacked or sewn in place. Remove the tacks or cut the thread, and save the padding. You may be able to use it again, or at least use it as a pattern for forming new pads.

The next step is to remove the inside arm covers. These also were tacked to the bottom rail. Begin by pulling them up through the frame, then removing the tacks which hold them to the back and front posts of the frame. Once again, observe carefully how these pieces were fitted to the piece. In particular, see how the front of the arm was formed, and how the fabric was fitted around the front and back posts.

Finally, remove the fabric and padding covering the seat. Look to see if the fabric of the seat has been made in two pieces. Frequently, the good final fabric is used to make the forward part of the seat piece (the first 6 to 8 inches), and a heavy muslin or other fabric is sewn to it and used to cover that part of the seat which is under the cushion.

With the cover fabric and padding removed, you now see the burlap covering the springs. You'll also see any roll edges which have been used. Remove the roll edges carefully, since you can reuse them. Take off the burlap, exposing the springs. If the chair hasn't been upholstered in a long time, it is likely that the twine tying the springs has rotted and broken. Cut away all of the old twine.

The springs have been sewn to the webbing in the bottom of the piece. Cut the thread which holds the springs in place, and lift them out. Finally, remove all of the old webbing by turning the piece over again and removing the tacks which hold it in place.

The piece has now been stripped to the bare frame. Before beginning the reupholstery job, examine the frame for damage. Fill any cracks with glue, and clamp them tightly while the glue dries. Replace any wood which cannot be repaired. If you want to refinish visible wood parts, do it now.

Reupholstering. If the piece has coil springs, the first step is to install new webbing across the bottom of the seat. If the piece has zig-zag springs, these will not have been removed during the stripping. Just check to see that all are solidly anchored in the frame. If any have come loose, you'll have to restretch them across the bottom, then renail them to the bottom rail.

Zig-zag springs are stiff and hard to stretch back into place after they have come loose. One way to do it is to set up a leverage situation. Make a loop about 4 in. in dia. of three or four lengths of heavy twine. Place this loop around the second zag from the loose end of the spring. Now insert a lever (use a long-handled hammer, a pry bar, etc.) through the loop. Pull the handle toward the outside of the frame until you can rest it against the outside of the frame. This will stretch the spring almost into position. Now slowly pull the top of the lever, with the bottom of it against the side of the bottom rail. This will pull the end of the spring into position over the rail. While you hold the lever firmly, have someone drive 1-in. nails or heavy staples through the holes in the spring clip into the chair rail.

To install webbing. To install webbing across the bottom of the piece, use a roll of 3½-in. jute webbing and No. 12 tacks. Plan to place strips of webbing just as they were in the original job—usually about 1 in. or less apart, with webbing strips run from front to back and from side to side, interwoven.

Place the first strip with about 1½ in. of the webbing extending beyond the outside of the

WELTING is used on most furniture. Make your own by folding a 2-in. strip of fabric around cording, then sewing close to the base of the cording.

AFTER COMPLETING the work on the seat, install any webbing needed to support the arms or back. This webbing should not be stretched in place.

rail. Drive four tacks to hold the strip in place (see photos), then fold over the extended end of the webbing and drive three more tacks. Now stretch the webbing across the seat opening. You won't be able to stretch it tight enough with your hands, so use a webbing stretcher to pull it as tight as you can. Hold the webbing tight with the stretcher while you drive four tacks to hold it. Now cut the webbing about 1½ in. outside of the rail and fold the cut end back across the rail. Drive three more tacks to complete the job. Install all the front-to-back strips of webbing first, then do the side-to-side strips. Interweave the side-to-side strips as you put them in place.

Installing the springs. Turn the chair right-side up and position the springs on the webbing inside of the seat. They should be spaced evenly and symmetrically. Use carpet thread and a large needle to sew the springs to the webbing. Begin by sewing the spring at one corner of the seat, using a long, continuous length of thread. Sew each spring to the webbing in four places, so that the thread makes a square pattern, then move on to the next spring. When you finish sewing, all springs will be firmly fixed to the webbing.

Next, the springs must be tied, using a 6-ply hemp twine. The twine is anchored to the chair rail by two No. 12 tacks driven at each end of a line of springs. The twine is tied to each spring as it passes over the coil, and as you tie each line of springs, you shape the seat, giving it a smooth, rounded contour. To do this, you compress the springs near the seat rails, and allow the springs to stand a little higher. Run the twine from front to back, then from side to side, tying it tightly to both sides of each spring.

Arm and back supports. In some cases the chair or sofa may have jute webbing as a support for the padding in the back or arms. Install this now by tacking the webbing strips in place. As a rule, this webbing is not stretched.

Burlap cover. Cover the newly tied springs with a layer of burlap, tacking it in place on the side rails. If edge rolls have been used to pad out or square up the front rail of the seat, install these now. Tack them in place, then sew them to the burlap cover.

Installation of padding. Next the padding of the seat is installed. This may be two layers—one of hair and one of cotton, separated by a layer of burlap. Or it may be just one full layer of cotton. Or it may be a shaped pad of polyurethane foam. Whatever the padding is, it should be positioned carefully because the final shape of the seat depends on how the padding is placed.

It is a good idea to anchor the padding in some way. You can tack or staple it to the side rails if it reaches that far, or you can stitch through it into the burlap beneath it in several places. These anchors prevent the possible slipping of the padding under the final cover.

The muslin cover. The best furniture has a cover of muslin over the padding, with the final cover fabric applied over the muslin. Because it is very costly (in terms of labor), not much furniture is made this way anymore. Instead, the final cover is applied right over the padding. But it is recommended that you do it because it makes the application of the final cover much easier also provides some additional protection for the padding.

The arms and back. Now move to the arms. Check the notes you made during the stripping of the piece to see how the padding was positioned

USE THE OLD FABRIC pieces as patterns to guide you in cutting the new fabric. Cut the new pieces slightly larger, then trim as needed.

HAND SEWING to join sections of the final cover is easy and makes for a smooth, good-looking job. Sew wherever tacking isn't practical.

and how the fabric was cut and tacked. At this time, simply rebuild each arm as it was before, using muslin as a cover, applying the final cover after the muslin.

When covering the arms, do the insides (that part facing into the seat), and then the outsides. The fabric goes down between the seat and the lower wood part of the arm, and is tacked to the bottom of the bottom rail. The outside arm piece most often is blind-tacked at the top, then stretched down the side and tacked to the bottom side of the bottom rail.

There are two tricky spots to watch for as you cover the arms. The first is cutting the fabric to fit around the arm and back posts. Check the old fabric to see how these cuts were made, and make the new cuts carefully. If you cut too much, you may spoil the fabric and be forced to make a new piece for the arm.

The second tricky place is the front of the arm. There are at least a dozen ways in which the front of the arm may be finished. The best way, until you have become proficient at upholstering, is to remake the arm exactly as it was before. Once again refer to your notes, and observe how the old fabric was cut and tacked or folded the first time. Sometimes the front is only tacked; other times, it may be sewn as well as tacked.

The inside and outside backs. After the arms are finished, proceed to the inside back. Put the padding in place, and anchor it by stitching. Cover it with muslin, and then with the final fabric. The inside back usually is tacked about two inches below the top of the outside of the back rail. It is then stretched over the top of the chair and down the front. At the bottom it is pushed through between the seat cover and the bottom back brace and pulled tight. The bottom edge is tacked to the bottom of the bottom rail.

The outside back now is blind-tacked at the top, pulled down tight across the back, and then tacked to the bottom of the bottom rail. As a rule, the sides of the outside back cover are sewn to the fabric of the sides with tight stitches.

Welting. No mention was made of welting until now because some chairs don't use it. However, if you use it, welting is tacked in place. It may be used, for example, to outline the back. If so, it is tacked in place after the arms and the inside back cover have been installed.

The dust cover. Once the final fabric is on, turn the piece over and tack black cambric to the bottom as a dust cover.

Protecting the fabric. After the upholstering has been finished, purchase a can or two of fabric protector spray and spray the completed work according to the directions on the can. This will help to protect the fabric from dirt and grease, make it easier to clean, and keep it new looking for a longer period.

Respring an upholstered chair

UNCLE CHARLIE sat down too hard, but don't blame him. The webbing was old and ready to go. You can see that someone once retied these springs with rope.

■ WHEN THE BOTTOM drops out of an upholstered chair or sofa, don't panic. The hanging springs and torn webbing may look like a bomb went off inside the upholstery, and the sagging seat may make the job look hopeless, but things aren't really as bad as they appear.

Unless the upholstery fabric itself is badly worn, you aren't faced with a huge bill for a complete reupholstering job. In fact, with a few materials and less than an hour's work, you can restore the piece to better than its original condition. Furthermore, you won't have to touch the upholstery fabric as you work, since all repairs can be made through the bottom.

Start by turning the chair or sofa upside down. Use a hammer and tack lifter to remove the torn dust cover and all of the old webbing. You may be tempted to leave any strands of webbing which aren't broken—but don't do it. Webbing usually breaks because it has rotted with age. If some of it broke, you can be sure that the rest will go soon, too. Plan to put in all new webbing.

Webbing is made of jute, is 4 in. wide, and you can buy it by the yard at most fabric stores. Count the number of strands used across the chair bottom, and then compute how much you will need, adding a yard or two to allow for stretching. Ten yards is more than enough for most chairs, but you may need 20 yards for a sofa.

In addition to the webbing, you should also buy a webbing stretcher, a magnetic tack hammer, a box of webbing tacks (No. 12s), some heavy thread (the kind used for sewing carpeting), and a large, curved sailmaker's needle. You'll find all of these items available in the upholstery section of large fabric stores.

Once the old webbing is off, probe into the seat and check the twine which was used to tie the springs. You'll have to reach up through the springs to get at it, and if any is broken or loose, cut it away and replace it. At the start, each of

AS THE TYING progresses, the springs stand up straight and no longer lean. When finished, each spring should have eight knots on its topmost coil.

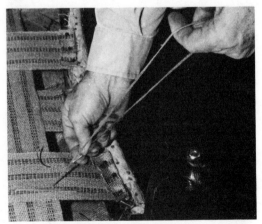

THE CURVED NEEDLE makes it easy to sew down through the webbing, around the top wire of the spring, and then back up through the webbing in one stitch.

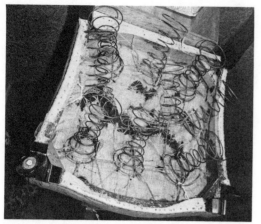

THE OLD WEBBING has been stripped away and you can see that the twine holding the springs is loose or missing. The springs are now loose and leaning.

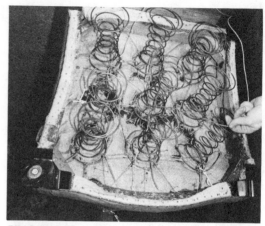

REACHING UP through the springs, use heavy twine to retie them. The ties connect the top wire of each coil to the neighboring coils.

THE WEBBING is tacked to the back rail, then stretched taut across the row of springs. Use the webbing stretcher to pull strand as tight as possible.

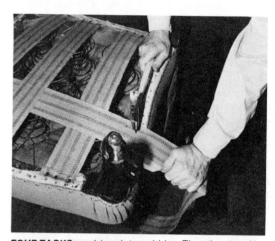

FOUR TACKS are driven into webbing. Then the strand is cut about 1½-in. outside of the tacks and the end is folded inward and secured with three tacks.

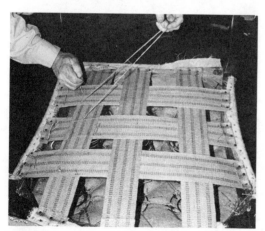

SEW THROUGH the webbing four times over each spring, making a square pattern, with the spring sewn to the webbing at each corner of the square.

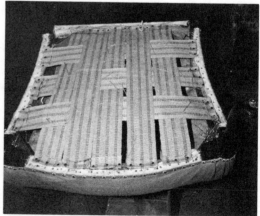

AFTER SEWING, you may want to attach several more strands of webbing to provide additional support for the seat. Here two more strands were tacked in place.

the springs may be leaning in a different direction. By the time you have finished repairing the ties, each spring should be standing up on its own.

This retying is one of the secrets of this type of repair. If you simply replace the webbing without retying the springs, the seat will be lumpy and uncomfortable.

With the springs tied, apply new strands of webbing. Put one across each row of springs from front to back, then do the same from side to side. To apply each strand, tack one end of the webbing to the frame, using the method shown in the pictures—four tacks, evenly spaced, then fold the end of the webbing over and drive three tacks.

Use your webbing stretcher to pull the strand tight across the row of springs. *Very* tight. You are compressing the springs up against the seat, so you'll have to pull the webbing tighter than you would if you were just starting the upholstery job and the springs were not in place. You want to end up with the webbing stretched flat across the bottom of the chair.

You may have to reach under and adjust the springs as you stretch, making sure each spring is upright and in contact with the webbing. Once the webbing is tight, tack the loose end to the frame and go to the next strand.

When you have all the strands of webbing in place both ways across the springs, get out the curved needle and the carpet thread. The curved needle makes it easy to sew through the webbing, around the top wire of each spring. You want to sew each spring to the webbing in four places.

The easiest way is to make a square pattern with the thread over each spring, sewing down through the webbing around the top spring wire at each corner of the square—then moving on to the next spring to begin another square. This sewing is important because it anchors the springs and assures you that they won't shift out of position as the chair is used. If the springs remain unanchored and do shift, the seat will sag or collapse.

You will note that in this method of repair you have not replaced the webbing strand for strand, but have simply installed strands over each row of springs. This is necessary so that the springs are compressed properly. However, you may end up with fewer strands of webbing than were originally used. You may want to install several additional strands after you have finished the sewing of the springs.

THE JOB is completed by tacking or stapling a dust cover of black cambric to the bottom. Note how flat the bottom is because the webbing was stretched tight.

Whether you do or not depends on the size of the piece and the strain which will be put on the webbing. In the chair pictured, two more strands of webbing were added because it was felt the chair seat needed additional support. As a general rule, there should be no more than 1 in. between strands of webbing to give adequate support.

Finally, tack a dust cover of black cambric in place, and your upholstered piece is as good as new—with only a small outlay of time and money. You'll find it convenient to staple the dust cover in place if you have a stapling gun. The work is quicker and, since the dust cover receives no stress, strength isn't necessary.

Hints for easier work. The inside of an upholstered seat can be pretty dusty and dirty. After taking off the old webbing, use one of the tube attachments on your vacuum cleaner to reach in and get rid of the dirt before proceeding.

When you buy jute webbing, get the amount you need in a continuous piece, buying a yard or two more than you know you'll need. Don't cut strips from the webbing roll. Instead, tack the loose end, then stretch the webbing across the seat, and tack it down. Then cut the webbing about 1½-in. beyond the row of tacks you drove. Using this method, you are always sure of having enough webbing available to apply the stretcher.

When retying the springs, keep in mind that they were originally tied eight ways. That is, the twine ran from the front to the back, from side to side, and in both diagonal directions, and was tied to each wire it passed over, making a total of eight ties to each spring.

In retying, you won't be able to run a continuous length of twine in each direction. But you can tie each spring to its neighbor individually and end up with the same eight-way type of tie. Heavy twine ideal for use in spring tying can be purchased in balls at the same time you buy your webbing.

THE PATTERN to follow when sewing the springs to the webbing is shown here. By making a square over each spring, the coil can be stitched four times.

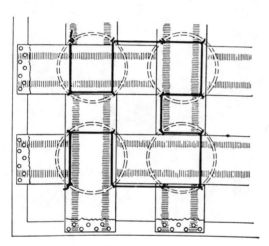

THE PATTERN followed in originally tying the springs produces eight ties on each spring. In repairing the seat, use the same number of ties.

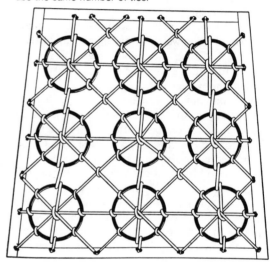

Auto upholstery repair

■ TIME CAN DO TERRIBLE THINGS to a car's upholstery. At first it's just a tiny split in a seam or a small stain. But before you know it, the whole interior looks bad.

The remedies range from mild (a set of seat covers) to wild (a custom reupholstery job). The one you choose may depend on the condition of your car's seats, how much you're willing to spend and how much of a perfectionist you are. Each of these extremes is illustrated here—the conservative job with a Honda Accord hatchback, the radical job with a 1957 Chevrolet sedan.

Seat covers: the quick facelift

The front-seat upholstery on a Honda Accord was scuffed but intact. The rear seat had two split seams, but the padding and springs were sound. The treatment decided on was a quick cover-up with seat covers.

Installing seat covers in a sedan requires removing both the rear seatback and the rear cushion. But since the hatchback allowed easy access to the rear of the seatback, only the cushion was removed.

The hatchback, however, did present a minor problem: The section of carpeting behind the rear seatback and over the rear cargo area had to come out before the seat cover could be slipped on. Since that section of carpeting was badly worn, it was replaced with a new polyester carpeting kit. Velcro fasteners and screw eyes had to be transferred from the old carpet piece to the replacement.

Stretching the fitted seat covers over the rear cushion and seatback was a straightforward job. Any wrinkles that developed were smoothed out working from the center outward.

Each cover has several elastic loops attached to its edges. The idea is to slip an S hook into each loop, stretch the elastic, and attach the hook to the springs. For extra security, you can pinch the open ends of the S hooks closed with pliers.

The front seats didn't need to be removed. The seat covers were slipped over the seatbacks and

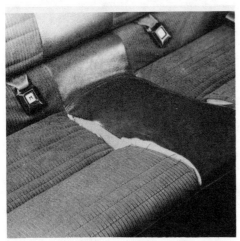

UPHOLSTERY IN THIS ACCORD shows what can happen if children use a car seat as a trampoline. Remove rear seat cushion to install the seat cover.

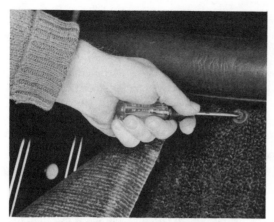

1. YOU HAVE TO REMOVE THE CARPETING from the rear seatback before you can install the seat cover in this car. Six screws hold the carpeting.

2. REAR SEAT CUSHIONS can be held down with bolts or a wire loop. Some release by pushing in at the lower front edge and pulling straight up.

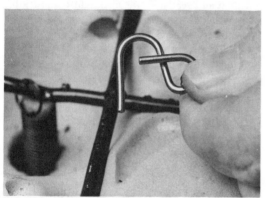

3. STRETCH COVER OVER SEAT and smooth wrinkles. Attach cover's elastic loops to spring with S hooks. Close hook's open end with pliers.

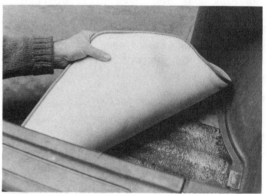

4. NEW CARPETING FOR THE CARGO AREA and rear seatback was the finishing touch of this budget restoration.

the elastic loops tied to the seat frame. The covers for the cushions were secured with S hooks from underneath.

These covers weren't tailored specifically for the Accord. One size was designed to fit several models, so the fit was not precise.

The cover for the rear cushion, for example, was a bit skimpy and required some adjustments for proper coverage of the entire top of the cushion. The rear seatback cover, on the other hand, was much more ample. Excess material had to be tucked in for a neat fit. A few extra elastic loops all around would have been welcome.

If the seats in your car are contoured, as they are in the Accord, it's probably best to leave enough slack in the covers so they sag into the contoured areas. Stretching the covers drum-tight may look neater, but the covers probably won't last as long.

Professional reupholstery job

If you'll settle for nothing less than a professional-looking upholstery job, you need an auto upholstery shop.

A professional job allows you to choose the material—vinyl, cloth or leather. You can specify whether you want pleats, diamond tufts or smooth panels.

If you're a purist, you can try to duplicate your car's original upholstery. Some popular upholstery materials, even from many years back, may still be available from suppliers and even car dealers. But such materials could be expensive.

Alternatively, the upholstery shop may suggest

another material that's very close to the original—and much cheaper.

A 1957 Chevrolet two-door sedan got the complete interior treatment from a professional upholstery shop with pleated maroon vinyl and black trim accents.

The shop first measured the seats carefully. Then they unbolted and removed both seats, separated the front seatbacks from the cushion and stripped away all the padding down to the frame and springs.

The front-seat padding was in a sorry state, but the springs were sound. The front seat cushion once had a layer of burlap over the springs to keep them from working through the upholstery, but the burlap had rotted away. It was replaced with a sheet of vinyl. Working from the center outward, the vinyl was stretched tight and at-

THE FRONT SEAT of this 1957 Chevrolet looked like a battle zone. Remove seat and peel off upholstery and padding down to bare frame and springs.

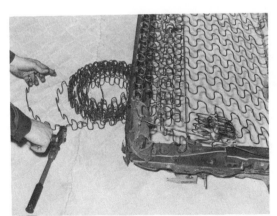

1. BROKEN SPRINGS MUST BE REPLACED. The spring material comes in large rolls. Cut off the length you need and, using pliers, attach it to seat frame.

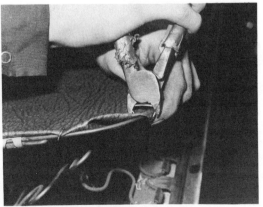

2. STRETCHING A SHEET OF VINYL over the springs keeps them in place. C-shaped hog rings, installed with hog-ring pliers, secure vinyl to the seat.

3. NOW FOR UPHOLSTERY: Lines marked at 2-in. intervals on back of vinyl are guides for pleats when foam is sewn on. Polyester thread is best.

4. UPHOLSTERY PANELS ARE STITCHED together and secured to seat with hog rings. If original padding is sound, new upholstery can slip on over old.

tached to the springs with C-shaped hog rings at rough 6-in. intervals.

Next came a sheet of jute carpet underpadding, a light coat of aerosol trim adhesive, and layers of 1-in. foam padding, cotton batting and Dacron cloth. Hog rings, installed with hog-ring pliers, secured each layer.

The most exacting task was stitching the pleated upholstery. Guide lines were scribed along the back of the vinyl at 2-in. intervals. The vinyl was stitched to a layer of 1-in. foam. Referring to the original seat measurements, the various upholstery panels were cut to the correct size and sewn together.

The seatback upholstery had to be a tight fit.

The covers were started inside out and unrolled over the seatback. A portable steamer—a small boiler with a hose and a wand—softened the vinyl when necessary so it could be adjusted for a perfect fit. Hog rings secured the upholstery to the seats.

The rear seat was much easier than the front. The original padding and springs in the rear seat were in good shape, so the new upholstery was simply installed over the old.

The Chevy's professional interior renovation cost several times that of the Honda's quick cover-up seat cover job. But those rich vinyl pleats and thick padding make the Chevy's seats look and feel better than new.

Vacation home plans

EVERYONE needs a hideaway to get away from it all. Only nowadays, it's got to be a hideout big enough for the rest of the gang.

And, when you consider that it also must be inexpensive, comfortable, trouble-free and adaptable to any location, the obvious solution is a vacation home—preferably one you can build with a minimum of time, skill and cash outlay.

With these points in mind, we took a good look at the vacation-home market, or as some prefer, the second-home industry. The result is this collection of homes you can build *now* and enjoy later.

The first home, as shown on these two pages, is a three-stage affair that can be built quickly in first-stage form, then expanded as the need arises. You could, however, complete all three stages at once, because the house is designed around the 4x8-ft. modular concept, and therefore requires a minimum of cutting during the actual construction.

The first stage basically is a simple shelter that doubles as a camping center. Add a cooking unit, water heater, shower, toilet and more deck area to convert the basic module into an easy-to-live-in cabin. To complete the third stage, enclose the living area, install a prefab fireplace, insulate if desired, and add those personal touches that make a home.

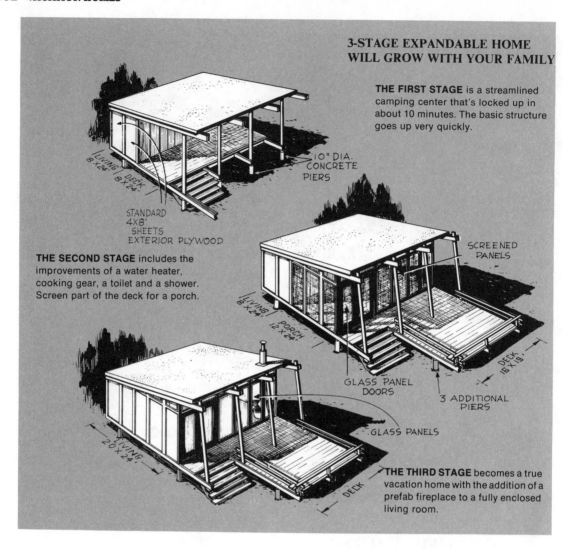

3-STAGE EXPANDABLE HOME WILL GROW WITH YOUR FAMILY

THE FIRST STAGE is a streamlined camping center that's locked up in about 10 minutes. The basic structure goes up very quickly.

LIVING DECK 8 X 24'

10" DIA. CONCRETE PIERS

STANDARD 4X8' SHEETS EXTERIOR PLYWOOD

THE SECOND STAGE includes the improvements of a water heater, cooking gear, a toilet and a shower. Screen part of the deck for a porch.

SCREENED PANELS

LIVING 8 X 24'

PORCH 12 X 24'

DECK 16 X 19'

GLASS PANEL DOORS

3 ADDITIONAL PIERS

LIVING 20 X 24'

GLASS PANELS

DECK

THE THIRD STAGE becomes a true vacation home with the addition of a prefab fireplace to a fully enclosed living room.

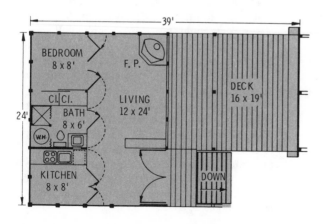

BEDROOM 8 x 8'

F. P.

39'

CL. CL.

LIVING 12 x 24'

DECK 16 x 19'

24'

BATH 8 x 6'

W.H

KITCHEN 8 x 8'

DOWN

SUPER CAMP

NOT EVERYONE with a piece of land wants—or needs—a true vacation home. Young weekenders especially find themselves "camping-out" and enjoying it more than reveling in a spectacular summer-home showcase.

A "super camp" such as this may be the answer. It will keep you dry on rainy afternoons, keep the wind out at night and minimize the need to pack up your outing equipment and bring it home.

The shelter fulfills three important requirements—it can be locked securely to discourage pranksters and vandals; it provides over 400 sq. ft. of enclosed living area, and perhaps most

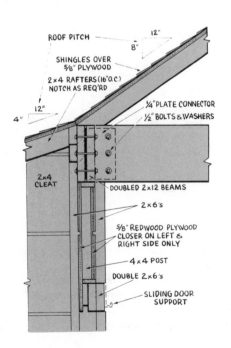

ROOF PITCH — 12"
8"
SHINGLES OVER 5/8" PLYWOOD
2 x 4 RAFTERS (16" O.C.) NOTCH AS REQ'RD
12"
4"
2 x 4 CLEAT
1/4" PLATE CONNECTOR
1/2" BOLTS & WASHERS
DOUBLED 2 x 12 BEAMS
2 x 6's
5/8" REDWOOD PLYWOOD CLOSER ON LEFT & RIGHT SIDE ONLY
4 x 4 POST
DOUBLE 2 x 6's
SLIDING DOOR SUPPORT

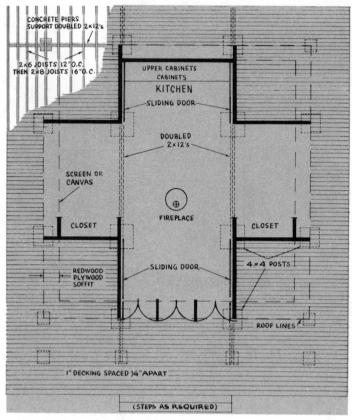

CONCRETE PIERS
SUPPORT DOUBLED 2×12's

2×6 JOISTS 12" O.C.
THEN 2×8 JOISTS 16" O.C.

UPPER CABINETS
CABINETS

KITCHEN

SLIDING DOOR

DOUBLED
2×12's

SCREEN OR
CANVAS

FIREPLACE

CLOSET

CLOSET

REDWOOD
PLYWOOD
SOFFIT

SLIDING DOOR

4×4 POSTS

ROOF LINES

1" DECKING SPACED ¼" APART

(STEPS AS REQUIRED)

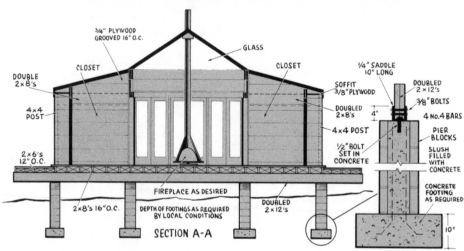

¾" PLYWOOD
GROOVED 16" O.C.

GLASS

DOUBLE
2×8's

CLOSET

CLOSET

¼" SADDLE
10" LONG

DOUBLED
2×12's

SOFFIT
3/8" PLYWOOD

3/8" BOLTS

4×4
POST

DOUBLED
2×8's

4 No.4 BARS

4×4 POST

PIER
BLOCKS

2×6's
12" O.C.

½" BOLT
SET IN
CONCRETE

SLUSH
FILLED
WITH
CONCRETE

FIREPLACE AS DESIRED

CONCRETE
FOOTING
AS REQUIRED

2×8's 16" O.C.

DEPTH OF FOOTINGS AS REQUIRED
BY LOCAL CONDITIONS

DOUBLED
2×12's

10"

SECTION A-A

important, it is a stylish structure with a pleasing appearance.

The clerestory above the entrance dramatizes the roofline and also provides good interior illumination. Similarly, a prefabricated fireplace adds interest to the center of the shelter, while providing a source of heat. Functionally, the closets and kitchen cabinets make "roughing it" a bit easier, and the sliding doors allow you to lock up the "camp" in a matter of minutes.

On following pages you'll find plans for other vacation cabins.

OCTAGONAL HOUSE—MODERN DESIGN WITH COMPLETE LIVABILITY

This high-style home adapts easily to beach, lakeshore or mountainside to provide a panoramic view of the surrounding territory.

What's more, since the house is shown here in three different sizes, it can fit a variety of needs and lot sizes. Just study the floor plans and pick the one that suits you best.

The smallest version of the octagonal house is basically a comfortable combination of a living-sleeping-dining area with separate bath and kitchen divisions, all built into a 309-sq.-ft. area. The next largest plan has a similar layout, but increases the total area to 483 sq. ft.

The largest of the three plans offers 768 sq. ft. and can be built as either a one-bedroom or two-bedroom house.

A roomy deck edges five of the eight sides of the house, adding spaciousness and guaranteeing a place to sun any time of the day.

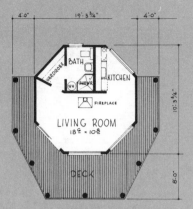

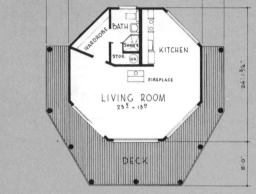

A BACHELOR with a small wooded site high in the mountains would be unlikely to find a better plan for a vacation home. It's comfortable and laid out for convenience, but has flair.

A LARGER VERSION of the octagonal design, this plan requires an additional five feet (in length and width) over the smaller version, yet has half again as much available living space.

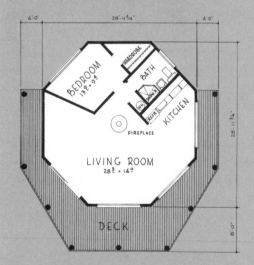

"A HOME AWAY FROM HOME" best describes this one-bedroom version of the eight-sided design. Although the deck rings five of the eight sides, amount of deck can be increased or decreased.

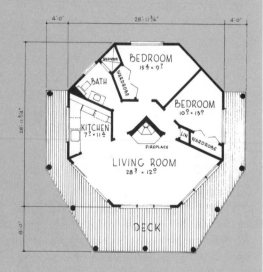

AS A YEAR-ROUND vacation home or a retreat solely for warm months, this two-bedroom version leaves little to be desired. Measurements shown in these plans are taken from extreme corners.

A-FRAME UPDATED FOR COMFORT

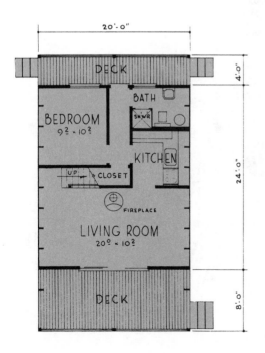

PRACTICAL layout of the A-frame is highly suitable for weekending the full year round. A front wall of glass allows full view of scenery and lets in plenty of daylight. Adding a rear door improves the traffic pattern.

Once considered a radical design innovation, the A-frame has become a classic among vacation home styles. The adaptability of the A-frame has much to do with its popularity, since it can be built on most any site and customized to reflect the owner's individuality.

The plan utilizes a large expanse of glass on the front to add spaciousness to the 645-sq.-ft. home (480 sq. ft. on lower floor, 165 sq. ft. on upper level), and includes an often-needed back door.

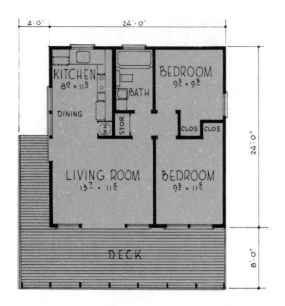

SLOPING ROOF ADDS EYE APPEAL

The weather-worthy shed roof has proven itself to be strong, durable and highly practical—and too often, extremely ugly.

However, thoughtful planning in the design stage has made the shed roofline appear clean and contemporary in this plan. Modestly sized, the house offers 576 sq. ft. of enclosed living space, an additional 272 sq. ft. of deck space, and an exterior that's fronted with supporting posts angled to break both the vertical and horizontal lines of the structure.

Inside, both bedrooms have a separate closet, and provision for a hot-water heater is made at one end of the kitchen.

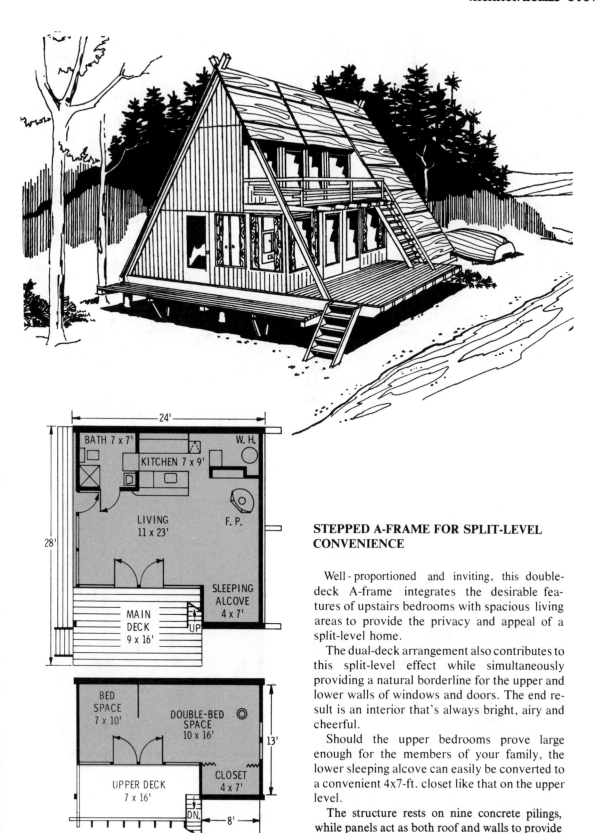

STEPPED A-FRAME FOR SPLIT-LEVEL CONVENIENCE

Well-proportioned and inviting, this double-deck A-frame integrates the desirable features of upstairs bedrooms with spacious living areas to provide the privacy and appeal of a split-level home.

The dual-deck arrangement also contributes to this split-level effect while simultaneously providing a natural borderline for the upper and lower walls of windows and doors. The end result is an interior that's always bright, airy and cheerful.

Should the upper bedrooms prove large enough for the members of your family, the lower sleeping alcove can easily be converted to a convenient 4x7-ft. closet like that on the upper level.

The structure rests on nine concrete pilings, while panels act as both roof and walls to provide the lateral rigidity required for an A-frame.

RIGID-FRAME CABIN FOR REMOTE HOMESITES

This cabin would make an ideal vacation home for your family or, if you are a hunter, a hunting lodge for you and some friends.

Its rigid-frame construction offers two distinct advantages. First, the cabin goes up in a hurry because all the framing members are identical and, thus, can be prefabricated before the actual erection. Second, the absence of load-bearing interior walls means the floor plan can be varied to suit any requirements without affecting the strength and rigidity of the cabin.

Although normal spacing of frame members is 2 ft. on centers, you could double up on each and space them 4 ft. o.c. for larger sidewall openings. Inside the cabin, the large frames can be left uncovered for a handsome "exposed beam" look. However, if you're already planning on next season's hunting, you can add insulation between the frames and then panel the interior with decorative plywood.

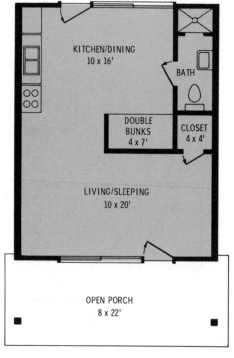

PALATIAL HIDEAWAY FOR PEACEFUL AFTERNOONS

Designed for easy building on remote sites, this luxurious retreat can be put together in a week, using preframed plywood panels and precut lumber.

When you're through, you have a vacation palace—a true second home—with 770 sq. ft. of enclosed living space and another 700 sq. ft. of outdoor deck space.

The attractive clerestory arrangement in the roof not only adds to the appearance of the house, but it also serves a utilitarian purpose by flooding the interior with light, even on cloudy days.

Another unusual feature is found in the living room, where hinged privacy panels drop from the ceiling to create three separate sleeping areas for weekend guests. Yet even when the panels are lowered, there's still plenty of space remaining around the fireplace for informal entertaining and relaxing. Using sliding doors throughout also adds a touch of casual elegance.

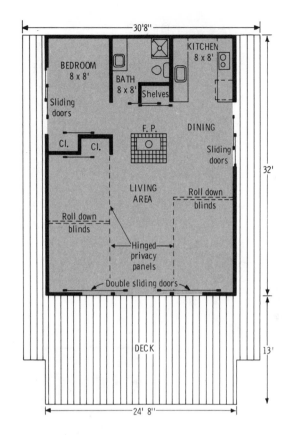

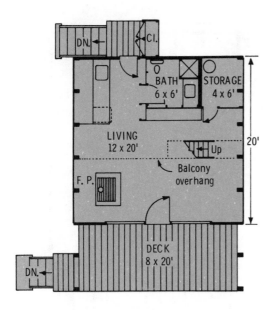

SPARTAN A-FRAME FOR RUGGED VACATIONERS

Nested atop a rocky mountain, this striking A-frame withstands gusting winter winds as well as sudden summer storms to make it an ideal weekend refuge.

To relieve the bare A-frame lines, an extra pair of frames and a canvas canopy extend over the deck to form a shelter from sun, rain and snow. Inside, a neat plastic skylight provides natural illumination, while the front wall of windows and door takes full advantage of the view.

The living room contains 240 sq. ft. of space with a prefabricated corner fireplace that's perfect for warming up after a hard day's skiing. The 144 sq.-ft. sleeping balcony overlooks the living area and is accessible via a shiptype stairway. The rear of the A-frame has a second entry (into the kitchen) on the lower level, while cool summer night breezes can enter the balcony area through a pair of swinging windows.

As with these homes, it's best to lay the foundation *in strict accordance with the plans* before the delivery of the other construction materials.

Summer houses

■ MANY HOUSES used to be built with a huge porch in front or off the side. On warm summer evenings you'd be likely to find a family sitting out there rather than inside a hot, stuffy house. Unfortunately, this is a thing of the past. One of these garden houses, or a combination of some of their features could bring back some old-time elements of outdoor living.

Keep off the grass

All three have one thing in common—a wood floor. This gets you up off the ground, provides a dance floor, and means that you don't have to balance a drink between two dandelions. But in each case, the floor has been taken a crucial step further. The most common pitfall of outdoor structures is that they frequently look as if they were dropped out of a plane onto your back yard. They just don't look as though they belong there. All these gazebos have extended flooring, as deck platforms, a balcony, or a ramp, past the structural lines of the building. This softens the look of the structure and makes it more a part of the ground it's on.

Aside from the design considerations, another tool that will make a good-looking site is landscaping. This is most obvious in the location of the canopy gazebo. The roof line, which might have looked quite severe if it were out in an open area, is successfully nestled in a stand of trees. The simplicity of the construction, using treated poles, is totally harmonious with the surroundings. On a smaller scale, the lines of the deck on the garden gazebo can be muted with shrubs or planter boxes.

All the deck platforms outside the 4x4 posts on the garden gazebo are made up from 2x8 structural-grade redwood. The interior of each box is framed 16 inches on center with short lengths, and 2x4s are face-nailed to form the deck. The dimensions are all modular (4x8, 3x12

Screen house: Pilings are used to support this structure in a unique setting by the water. The design of a screen house beats mosquitoes in back yards, too

Garden gazebo: This back-yard house is so versatile that it can be elegant for entertaining, informal or used strictly by the gardener with the green thumb

Canopy gazebo: This simple canopy has lines which are perfectly elegant and simple. The construction blends in beautifully on a wooded site

SCREEN HOUSE

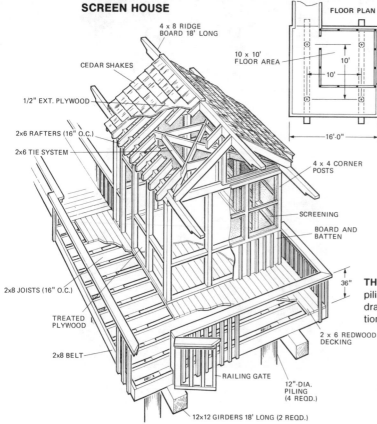

4 x 8 RIDGE BOARD 18' LONG

CEDAR SHAKES

1/2" EXT. PLYWOOD

2x6 RAFTERS (16" O.C.)

2x6 TIE SYSTEM

4 x 4 CORNER POSTS

SCREENING

BOARD AND BATTEN

2x8 JOISTS (16" O.C.)

TREATED PLYWOOD

2x8 BELT

RAILING GATE

2 x 6 REDWOOD DECKING

12"-DIA. PILING (4 REQD.)

12x12 GIRDERS 18' LONG (2 REQD.)

36"

FLOOR PLAN

10 x 10' FLOOR AREA

10'

10'

10'

16'-0"

16'-0"

GARDEN GAZEBO

WORKING garden center is at the rear of the garden gazebo. Lattice doors on rubber wheels slide away to reveal a solid potting counter and plenty of storage space.

THE 10x10-FT. screen house is offset on the 16x16-ft. piling frame, thus creating pleasant deck space. The drawing at left gives good bird's-eye view of construction.

YOU CAN EVEN plant your garden around the gazebo. The 3x10-ft. deck units can be built to use as ramps or a walkway which leads through the garden.

THE TRELLIS roof is made up of 2x2s in frames. This puts filtered light on the deck of the gazebo or you can use plywood for shade.

ONE SECTION of deck was not completed so the lawnmower could be wheeled into the "closet." More storage area for pots is located under the bench.

HOW ABOUT piling up some pillows and settling back on one of the benches for a sunbath? This corner deck is great to use for flowering plants too.

CANOPY GAZEBO

ONCE YOU'VE SUNK the four poles in the ground, construction can move quickly. Double girders, supported through the poles, are used to support conventional 2x8 joists. Single upper carriers support the roof. Construction techniques are simple but yield a strong and sturdy structure.

and so forth) so there is absolutely no material waste. These platforms are so dimensionally stable that they don't need footings. They can rest securely on level ground and you can arrange them in any way you prefer. A few well-placed toenails will hold one in place as a bridge that rests on two other decks to create different levels.

The roof of the garden gazebo is designed for a dry climate; 2x4-ft. panels are made up using 2x2s to form a lattice. This will cut the direct sun but still keep the light, airy feeling you want outside. Depending on the climate where you live, part of the roof could be solid. The lattice panels fit into the roof framing system and can be removed for a piece of plywood if you want more protection. Although the plans don't include wir-

ing diagrams, you can run a code-approved line from your house out to the shelter. A few simple boxes with floodlights will make it look like a dream house at night and let the party keep going well after dark. Install at least one duplex receptacle (grounded) for a radio, TV, warming tray or coffeemaker.

Select your location

To get the most use from your garden house, it has to be located close enough to the main house so you can easily bring out food and drink. It can't be far away from the garden or you'll spend too much time going back and forth with a wheelbarrow. It makes sense to try for a site in between. Check these guidelines.

Sighting-in on a site

- **Don't sink a pole** or pier over any underground piping or septic tank.
- **Don't build in a natural grade depression** that collects ground water.
- **Don't build too close** to your property line. Check local codes.
- **Do look for a natural rise.** To get good drainage and minimum settling.
- **Do plan ahead for access,** walkways, ramps and any electric lines.
- **Do consult local building codes.** Make sure your site is legal.

Good sense and good cents

If possible, try to keep construction time to a minimum. A smart move is to cover the surrounding lawn area with polyethylene for the few days needed, or build yourself a simple gangway into the construction area. On most jobs, the surrounding area takes such a beating that it needs major "renovating" after the building is done. The more foliage you can preserve during the job, the more natural the garden house will look on its site. Keeping the area reasonably clean can avoid reseeding or buying new sod.

Keep a long-range point of view

- **Don't leave materials** stacked on the lawn or you won't have one when you're done.
- **Don't cut** through major roots of adjacent trees. Try a few test holes.
- **Don't underbuild** the frame or leave it unsealed. It's outside all year round.
- **Do protect trees and foliage** while building so they will be intact when you're done.
- **Do use** preservative-treated timbers for all framing in contact with the ground.
- **Do install** ground fault indicator fused circuits. It's national code for exteriors.

Don't be a fair-weather carpenter. Make those toenails count. Use galvanized nails to avoid rust streaks on the wood. Try 10d nails on face-nailed decking instead of 8d. The extra bite will help minimize warping and cupping. In short, build your garden house to withstand the worst storm in 20 years. In the end, you'll save on maintenance and repairs and be able to see the results of your labors on a good-looking job.

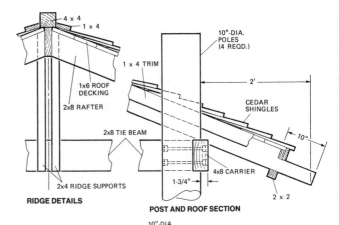

RIDGE DETAILS

POST AND ROOF SECTION

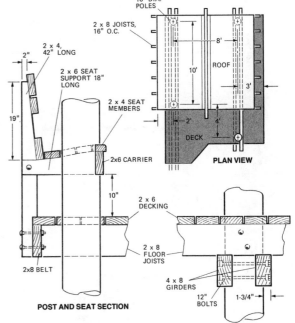

PLAN VIEW

POST AND SEAT SECTION

POST AND FLOOR SECTION

Close up your vacation home

■ WHEN THE END of summer approaches, the time comes to think about "battening down the hatches" at a vacation home which will be unattended during the winter months.

Many of the closing-down chores are things you've done year after year, and most of the items listed on these pages are simply common sense. But, if you make up a list and assign each member of your family specific tasks, the closing-down will go a lot faster—without a

chance of missing any important items.

You can usually hire a local resident who, for a nominal fee, will keep an eye on your place during your absence. To avoid misunderstandings, agree upon the fee and what services you expect to be done.

Finally, check your homeowner's insurance policy to see if any conditions must be met to assure your policy remains in full force during your absence.

Grounds, dock and boat check

Start with inspection of house exterior and grounds. Look for, and remove, broken or dead tree limbs or trees which may be leaning dangerously toward your house. Your "check-list" tour should include the following:
1. Clean out gutters and leaders.
2. Repair any loose roof shingles.
3. Point up any loose chimney bricks.
4. Clear *all* accumulation from the crawl-space area.
5. See that garbage cans have properly fitting covers. Scrub the cans with disinfectant and soap and water. When dry, store them out of the weather. Throw out damaged and uncovered cans.
6. Keep out varmints by covering chimney flues with a galvanized sheetmetal cap, securely fastened. *Immediately, upon fastening flue cover,* go inside and put a *big sign* on the fireplace to assure you *uncover flues* prior to use next season.

If possible, your boat should be drydocked. This may be: 1) at the local marina, 2) at your year-round home after a trailer tow or 3) stored on your vacation-home property. Items 1 and 2 simplify your task considerably. If you elect to do your own storing, follow these simple guidelines: Pick an area near the house on the opposite side from prevailing winds. A small boat can be inverted and stored on sawhorses; just make certain it is lashed down securely with a stout cord. With boat stowed, check your dock, mooring lines and accessories for any loose gear which may be stored in and lashed to the boat.

There's work to be done inside too

Scatter a liberal number of mothballs around the house, in each room. Mothballs will be easier to gather than flakes next spring. Also place mothballs between mattresses and springs. Since camphor evaporates when exposed to air, you may wish to have your "caretaker" replenish the supply every six weeks or so. *Do not set rodent traps.* Decomposition over the winter can cause

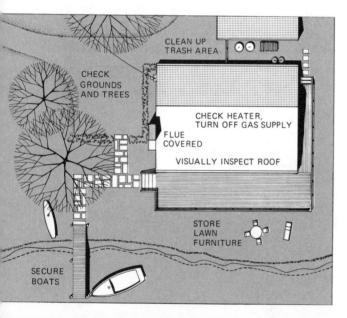

CLEAN UP
TRASH AREA

CHECK
GROUNDS
AND TREES

CHECK HEATER,
TURN OFF GAS SUPPLY

FLUE
COVERED

VISUALLY INSPECT ROOF

STORE
LAWN
FURNITURE

SECURE
BOATS

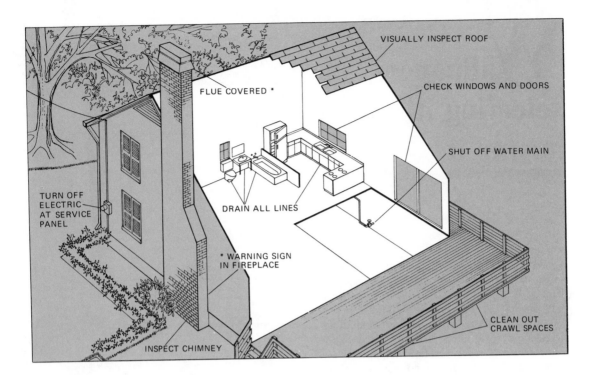

VISUALLY INSPECT ROOF

CHECK WINDOWS AND DOORS

FLUE COVERED *

SHUT OFF WATER MAIN

TURN OFF
ELECTRIC
AT SERVICE
PANEL

DRAIN ALL LINES

* WARNING SIGN
IN FIREPLACE

CLEAN OUT
CRAWL SPACES

INSPECT CHIMNEY

an odor that will be difficult to eliminate. A strong camphor odor will deter most rodents from entering the house.

Clean out all foodstuffs. Food packed in cardboard containers (cereals, flour and the like) will attract rodents and other vermin. Foods packaged in cans and bottles may be subject to below-freezing temperatures and stand a good chance of exploding. At best, they will probably outlive their shelf lives if left behind. Your best bet is to remove all food from your vacation home before leaving. For economy, of course, bring home what you can. Add what you decide isn't worth packing to the pile of trash that is to be hauled to the dump.

Before locking the front door, make a final check to assure that all combustible materials—paints, solvents, cleaning fluids, matches and the like—are removed from the house. Turn the heater switch to off, shut off the gas supply at the main and pull the main electric fuse (or trip the breaker). Finally, check screens, windows and doors to make certain they are firmly secured and locked.

Shut off water-supply main and drain *all* water-supply lines. Open valves on fixtures, drain fittings at their lowest points and leave valves open. A small amount of water may remain in the valves. To remove it, rig a section of hose to the pressure side (outlet) of your vacuum cleaner and blow out the fixtures. If your summer home is closed while the climate is still moderate, small amounts of water remaining in valves and lines left open will evaporate prior to freezing weather. Drain or siphon water from the toilet-bowl tank and remove the last bit with a sponge. Pour about a cup of permanent-type antifreeze in every trap. (Don't forget, the bathtub drain has a trap too.) Pour *two* cups of antifreeze in the toilet bowl. Waterpump and well-point systems vary depending upon the type installation. Here, it is best to have your plumber show you what to do the first time around. Write down what he tells you for use next year. (You may have a foot-valve type point, a flexible submersible point, or other: "Breaking" the vacuum by needless loosening of fittings can shorten the life of the fitting.)

Final points: Make certain your washed-down refrigerator is propped open. Also, it is worth the few dollars more your caretaker will charge to have him clear the driveway after each snowfall. In the event that fire should break out while the house is closed, a clear access could spell the difference between minimal damage and total loss.

Wallpaper: selecting it, buying it

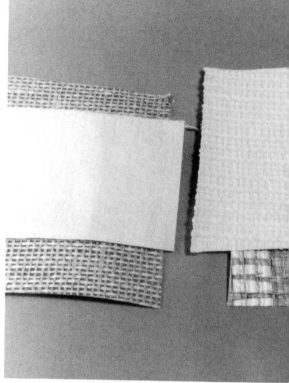

FABRIC AND GRASS PATTERNS usually have a paper backing to which the wallpaper paste is applied. If not, paste the wall and then embed the fabric into the paste.

■ "WALLPAPER" IS A TERM that applies to any flexible paper or fabric that is hung on a wall. That is, the covering doesn't have to be paper. It may be a foil or fabric such as aluminum or burlap—or even a fancy bed sheet. With modern adhesives and more attention being given to the manufacture of wall coverings, wallpapering has been greatly simplified. It is not easy to wallpaper. But it isn't especially difficult, either. Your big problems will be in matching the pattern as you go along and trimming around obstructions built into or out of the wall surface.

Wallpaper is truly a great cover-up. It can hide unsightly walls where paint can't. It is the middle ground between paint and paneling. The width and length of the paper lets you cover lots of area fast. And, once up, very little maintenance is required—perhaps just an occasional light washing with mild household detergent and water or a wallpaper cleaner.

Some home center stores sell wallpaper. A few hardware stores stock it. Your best bet probably is a store specializing in wallpaper, or a retail paint store that sells wallpaper as a sideline. Selection and inventory in some stores may be sketchy. You may have to order the product you want from a wallpaper book and then wait several days for delivery. In specialty stores, you may be able to pick what you want right out of the bin, but the types and designs of the paper can be limited.

Wallpaper types

There are eight basic types of wallpaper:

1. Lining paper
2. Vinyl wallpaper
3. Standard wallpaper
4. Foil papers
5. Fabric coverings
6. Flocked papers
7. Miscellaneous coverings
8. Prepasted wallpaper

Expect to find bargains during the summer months and from December to February as these are the times when retailers generally put wall coverings on sale.

The vinyl papers are a smart choice for kitchens, bathrooms, hallways, and kids' rooms where moisture, dirt, grease, crayon, and other soiling agents can be a problem. The "soft-faced" papers are perhaps more for decoration than the slick-coated papers, although the flocks and fabrics can be used almost anywhere.

Wallpaper can have any design, and some of the patterns almost glow in the dark. If you are a first-time paper hanger, you may want to stick with a plain paper or a paper that has geometric designs that are fairly easy to match. Striped patterns are probably the easiest for a beginner to hang, with little waste and matching involved. You simply cut the paper to the length you want, paste it, hang it, and then trim it at the top and bottom. The fabric-type papers can be fairly easy to match, too, but burlap can be tough since the weave has to be carefully matched where the cross weaves join. On patterned papers, you will see the word "repeat." What this means is that the pattern is repeated at intervals along the roll. Usually, the dealer will know the repeat spacing, or it may be noted in the manufacturer's sample book. For instance: The paper repeats every 20 inches. Your wall is 100 inches from the floor to the ceiling. Divide the 20 inches into the 100 inches and you'll get 5 inches or 5 repeats. In this instance, there will be little or no selvage for trimming; the repeat is a perfect match for the wall. However, another pattern may repeat more often, resulting in substantial waste. To avoid this, you want the number of repeats to closely fit the height of the wall.

Following is a selection guide to wallpapers that explains where various papers are best used and which adhesive should be used to hang the papers you are considering. This is a general guide. Be sure to discuss your project with the dealer before making a buying decision.

Lining paper

Lining paper looks like a roll of regular wallpaper (or even plain newsprint) with no pattern. Lining paper is used to "line" cracked and damaged walls before the decorative paper is installed. Lining paper, which sometimes is called "blank paper," also forms a wonderfully smooth base for the adhesive on the decorative paper and aids adhesive drying. You hang lining paper just like the standard stuff. Use butt joints at the edges of the paper and trim it at the ceiling and baseboard. At jambs, casing, moldings, and so on, leave the edge of the lining paper about ¼-inch from the molding surfaces. This little gap will let the top paper bond directly to the wall surface and help prevent it from peeling back as it might over lining paper in this application. Lining paper also can be used to cover patterns that would otherwise show through the new paper. However, if at all possible, remove old wallpaper before hanging new wallpaper. The less paper thickness on the wall, the better.

Vinyl wallpaper

Within this classification there are three basic types of wallpaper: vinyl that is affixed to paper; vinyl that is affixed to a cloth backing; and vinyl that has been impregnated into the backing like creosote is pressurized into wood timbers. The vinyl papers are probably the most durable of all wallpapers. You can scrub them with mild household detergents and they are tough to scratch, which makes them ideal for hallways, kids' rooms, and other high-traffic areas.

In the showroom, you may find wallpaper tagged "vinyl-coated." This is not a vinyl paper as such; the paper has been treated with vinyl on its face side and it can be a problem to clean. It is not very resistant to dirt, grime, oil, crayon, or grease.

The vinyls are sold in single, double, and triple rolls in widths from 18 to 27 inches. The length of the paper is always figured with the width so each single roll gives you a total of 36 square feet of wallpaper. Waste on a single roll will be approximately 6 feet, so allow for this in your measurements. You can also buy some vinyls in widths up to 54 inches and lengths up to 30 yards, but this material probably will require a special order, so expect to pay a bit more and wait several weeks for delivery. For the vinyls, use a mildew-resistant type adhesive. The vinyl papers are heavy and, therefore, tend to hold moisture vapor generated from normal household functions. Up to 30 gallons of moisture vapor are generated daily in normal household activities. This vapor has to escape, so it usually goes out windows, doors, and exhaust fans, or through the walls if the walls are not properly insulated. Although blocked by insulation when wallpaper is present, the moisture can cause wallpaper adhesives to mildew (behind heavy papers) and therefore a mildew-resistant adhesive should be used.

Vinyl paper also has another plus. It can be stripped very easily from walls and ceilings in the event you tire of it or want to use it elsewhere in your home. Or, you can reroll it and store it for later use. The vinyl papers are applied just like any other paper, with one exception. Vinyl will not stick to itself. Therefore, the laps have to be double cut and butted.

Standard wallpaper

This category is made up of vinyl-coated, cloth-backed, and just plain untreated paper. The standards usually sell for less than the more fancy coated papers. However, there is nothing wrong with the standard papers. They are not as durable as the others, so, if you buy them, consider them for areas that won't get hard usage. For example, a hallway wouldn't be a good choice. The standard measurements are the same as for the vinyl wallpapers. For hanging, we suggest either wheat paste or stainless cellulose adhesive. Both types are stocked by most retailers who sell wallpaper.

Be careful when hanging the standard papers. The paste tends to make the paper soggy and prone to rips and tears. Also, some *very* inexpensive standard papers may be unwashable or uncleanable. The ink patterns on the surface of the paper can dissolve or run when they become wet.

Foil papers

Foil wallpaper comes in two types: a metallike material that has been laminated to a backing, and an aluminum that has been laminated to paper. They look fairly similar. You'll be reminded of aluminum cooking foil with a design printed on one side. Foil conforms to wall surfaces like vinyl sheet flooring conforms to floors. Every little lump and bump will show through the surface, so the wall must be in super shape and sanded as smooth as possible. A foil application is best when done over lining paper. The lining paper will provide the smooth surface you want.

Use the same (mildew-resistant) adhesive for installing the lining paper and the foil. The liner will help speed the drying time of the adhesive. Foil papers will crease—like aluminum foil—so be especially careful hanging them. Also, some foil papers are stuck to the adhesive on the wall instead of covered with adhesive and stuck to the wall or other surface. Ask the dealer about this. Or, check the foil package which usually notes any special handling data.

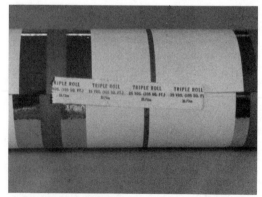

SOME PAPERS, like this foil, come in triple rolls with a yield of about 105 yards. Single rolls and double rolls are standard at most retailers. You sometimes can get a tad more than 30 square feet from a roll if the pattern is a stripe or very plain. But don't skimp in your estimates more than about 2 square feet.

Fabric coverings

Grass cloth, rice cloth, burlap, and hemp are all in this general classification. For the most part, all fabrics are laminated to a paper-type backing, although you can buy the fabric without backing and stick it up as an accent design. The fabrics with the paper backing, however, are much easier to handle than those without the backing.

The fabrics have some "dos" and "don'ts" you should know before buying them. Fabric colors sometimes vary between rolls of the same material. For example, you may see a nice, deep brown roll, but the same covering located in the same bin made by the same manufacturer may be a different color brown and not match the other rolls perfectly. But this doesn't necessarily need to be a problem. A mismatched color can often offer texture and color highlights that are pleasing. As you cut the fabric for hanging, you can lay it out flat on the floor and check any texture or color pattern. Then, interchange the strips and hang them to suit your taste.

Line the walls before applying any of the fabrics. You'll get better results and have an easier time of it even though you will spend a little extra time and money. However, if you don't line the walls, the walls must be sealed with a wall sizing. (Use a glue sizing sold in wallpaper departments.) Sized walls will not absorb the water in the adhesive as rapidly, and you can slide the fabric here and there for the proper fit. You generally do not have to match patterns with fabric. Allow about two inches for trimming purposes, however. This trimming figure should be included in your buying estimates. Wheat paste or liquid cellulose adhesive should be used for hanging fabrics. But again, check with the dealer.

Flocked wallpaper

You can buy this material with the flocking stuck to paper, vinyl, or foil. Paper is the least expensive of the three. There is no special trick to hanging this material but you must be careful not to damage the flocking by rubbing it. If you get adhesive on the flocking (which you will) blot it off with a damp sponge; don't try to rub it off or you will rub off or damage the flocking. You can use a vinyl or mildew-resistant adhesive for the flocks, but, of course, check with the dealer.

Prepasted wallpaper

These paper products are what their name implies: prepasted and ready to hang after the rolls are soaked in a special water box provided by the manufacturer/dealer. The selections include "standard" wallpaper, vinyl, foil, and flocked papers. If you haven't applied wallpaper before, the prepasted papers may be your best bet because they save lots of time and eliminate the cleanup you would have with adhesives. However, the prepasting is not always perfect: You may have to add paste to corners and seams as the paper goes up. Use the adhesive recommended earlier for the specific paper type.

Wallpaper squares for accents are also available in prepasted designs. The squares resemble tiles that are twelve-by-twelve inches square. The squares are extremely easy to paste up almost anywhere. However, you must lay out the wall the same way you would lay out a floor or a wall for ceramic tiles. If the first square doesn't go on the surface perfectly, the others will go on askew and the error will compound itself.

Miscellaneous wall coverings

Murals are sold in rolls with widths up to 36 inches. They can be from 10 to 12 feet long (and even longer), and often have matching paper or "backgrounds" to hang over, under, and at the sides of the murals. A mildew-resistant or vinyl adhesive is recommended for hanging. Bolt goods are laminated to paper backings, and are either ready-to-paste or prepasted. Goods such as burlap come in bolts (sometimes in rolls) 45 inches wide with special-order material measuring up to 54 and 60 inches. It usually is sold by the yard rather than the piece. The adhesive recommended is powdered vinyl or double-faced tape. If the fabric is laminated to a backing, the best adhesive is wheat paste or cellulose adhesive applied with a brush to the wall or the back of the material.

There are still other coverings, including real leather, which are sometimes available in stores, but usually are special-order items. A partial list would include cork, wood veneers, gypsum wallboard with a fabric covering, and Paris tile, a very thin vinyl wall covering that resembles floor sheet goods.

Estimating your needs

Before you go shopping for wallpaper, you should know how much you will need, where the product will go, whether or not you'll use a border, and what wall repairs will be needed before the material is applied. Intensive preplanning can save you hours of time and put you in a better bargaining position at the store since you'll be ready with nomenclature, sizes, amounts, and so on. In figuring room measurements, be aware of these considerations:

• Wallpaper comes in different widths. However, regardless of the width, each single roll will contain 36 square feet of wallpaper.

• The width of the wallpaper will determine the length of the wallpaper per roll. If the roll is wide, the length will be shorter. Therefore, you must consider the length needed in order to avoid horizontal joints across the area.

• Although there are 36 square feet of wallpaper in each single roll, the actual yield from the roll will be approximately 30 square feet. This, of course, is an average. The yield could be slightly more or slightly less than the 30 square feet figure. But estimate your needs at 30 square feet.

• Figure the entire room (or wall) when estimating. If there are doors, windows, or fireplaces cut into the wall, you should subtract one-half of a roll of wallpaper per door and window. Each opening is estimated to be about 18 square feet.

Trim or border paper that goes around the walls at the ceiling is usually sold by the yard. Figure the amount, in yards, around the room, and then buy one extra yard of border. For example, if the figure is 10 yards, buy 11 yards. You will need the extra for cutting and fitting.

Wallpaper adhesive usually is sold by the package which can weigh from one to five pounds. You can figure that one pound of dry mix adhesive is enough to hang six to eight rolls of wallpaper. However, you may need more, depending on paper, since some vinyl papers take more adhesive than others. Ask the dealer about this. A good rule of thumb is one gallon of vinyl adhesive for two to four rolls of paper. The lesser amount is for heavier vinyl wall coverings.

There are two types of wall or wallpaper sizing: wallpaper paste and a product termed "wall" or "wallpaper sizing." Simply, sizing seals the wall surfaces so water from the wallpaper adhesive isn't absorbed quickly producing "dry" voids behind the wall covering. The sizing also is like a paint primer: It gives the surface a "tooth" to which the adhesive sticks better. You can apply sizing with a paintbrush or a roller. It goes on very easily; there is no special application technique. Let the sizing dry thoroughly before you hang the paper.

Tools and equipment to hang wall coverings are readily available. In fact, most dealers sell a kit of tools specially assembled for the job. The tools are not top line, as a rule. So, if you

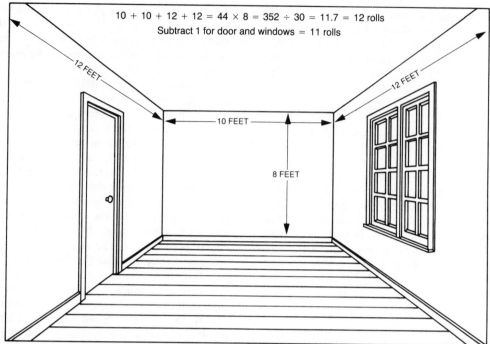

10 + 10 + 12 + 12 = 44 × 8 = 352 ÷ 30 = 11.7 = 12 rolls
Subtract 1 for door and windows = 11 rolls

12 FEET

12 FEET

10 FEET

8 FEET

TO ESTIMATE a room for wallpaper needs, measure the height of the room and the perimeter around the room. Here is a typical example. Two sides of the room are 12 feet, or a total of 24 feet. Two ends of the room are 10 feet, or a total of 20 feet, for a combined total of 44 feet. The ceiling/floor height is 8 feet. So 44 x 8 divided by 30 feet (the number of square feet in a roll of paper) equals 11.7. You would need 12 rolls. But there is a door and window. Subtract one-half of a roll for each. Net total for the project would be 11 rolls. This measurement is based on a single roll figure. See estimating chart.

will hang lots of wallpaper, we suggest that you buy professional equipment. The cost is not prohibitive.
You will need the following items:

- Water bucket
- Pasting table
- Wide adhesive brush
- Adhesive bucket

- Tape measure
- Utility knife with lots of replacement blades
- Trimming wheel
- *Metal* straightedge
- Chalk line and plumb bob
- Very sharp scissors with long blades
- Wallpaper smoothing brush
- Stepladder (six feet is a good size)

QUICK REFERENCE TO WALLPAPER ROLLS NEEDED

Feet Around Room	Single Rolls/Rooms			Single Rolls/Ceiling
	8 ft.	9 ft.	10 ft.	
36	9	10	11	3
40	10	11	13	4
44	11	12	14	4
48	12	14	15	5
52	13	15	16	6
56	14	16	17	6
60	15	17	19	7
64	16	18	20	8
68	17	19	21	9
72	18	21	22	10

- Wallpaper seam roller
- Drop cloths
- Wall sizing

You probably have many of these items in your workshop. If not, any necessary additions probably can be used for other types of home maintenance and improvement projects, so the investment can go a long way.

There is, perhaps, one exception: a pasting table. Ideally, a regular table for pasting wallpaper is recommended. You may be able to rent a table. If not, the cost of buying a table for just one wallpapering job would be prohibitive. If this is the case, you can use a regular folding table or even a floor surface (hardwood or tile). The pasting area must be smooth and clean and not covered with newspaper. (The ink on newspaper will float off onto the wallpaper when it becomes damp and wet.) You will overlap the width of wallpaper rolls with adhesive. After each roll, this excess adhesive should be wiped off the pasting surface with a damp cloth or sponge.

Wall preparation

The walls for wallpaper, as noted above, must be in good repair. The tools needed for this are listed in the sections on interior/exterior painting, and include putty knives, scrapers, spackling compound, sandpaper, and sanding blocks.

You can hang paper over painted glossy walls, but the gloss should be buffed flat with abrasives. Be sure the surface is not slick. You can also hang new wallpaper over new gypsumboard walls, but the gypsumboard covering (a paper) must be sealed first either with wall size or a good flat latex primer. The primer is recommended; let it dry and then lightly sand the surfaces with medium-grit paper on a block.

You will, no doubt, want to paint the trim molding in the room to match the wallpaper background or design color. If so, paint this trim *before* you hang the new wallpaper.

You can hang new wallpaper over old wallpaper, but it is not recommended that you do so. Any old wallpaper should be removed so you can start anew. Removing old paper is easy to say, but hard to do. There are three methods:

1. Rent a sprayer and spray water over the wallpaper surface until the paper can be scraped off the wall. Wallpaper dealers sell a solution to add to the water which speeds the softening process. This is a slow procedure, and a wet one, but it is effective.

2. Apply water mixed with a softening solu-

A LONG-T-SQUARE makes an excellent straightedge for cutting any wall covering. The tongue of the T is long enough to span the width of most wall coverings. Use a sharp razor knife or utility knife to cut the paper or fabric. Do not use scissors, except for special trimming where you can't use a knife blade. Change the knife blade often. A dull blade will crinkle the covering and skip, causing alignment problems.

BUY A WALLPAPER PASTE BRUSH even though the paper you will hang is prepasted. You will need extra paste on the paper, regardless. A piece of wire coat hanger makes an excellent brush holder. Cut it to fit the bucket and run the wire through the handle bails, as shown. If you leave the brush in the paste, the bristles will become very soggy and moplike.

tion with a brush. Plan on spending hours.

3. Rent a wallpaper steamer with a steam plate. The steaming method is the easiest of the three, although you will have to pay for the rental equipment. The price may be worth it.

The steamer will have three parts: boiler, hose, and steamer plate. The boiler is filled with water, which is heated into steam. The steam pressure is forced through the hose connected to the steamer plate. The plate has holes in it through which the steam is forced out and onto the wallpaper. The heat melts the adhesive and softens the paper, which is scraped off the surface. Most steamers are electrically operated; just plug the cord into an outlet and flip the switch.

The best time to operate a steamer is when it is cool—fall, winter, or spring. The machine generates lots of steam heat, so if you use it in the summer months, have plenty of ventilation.

Steamers are so efficient that you may not even have to scrape off the softened wallpaper—or at least not very much of it. The paper actually separates from the adhesive and the force of gravity makes it peel right off. You just have to help the peeling here and there with a slip or two of the scraper. There are also additives you can buy to mix with the water that is used to make steam. In reality, this is more of a gimmick than an aid.

Before you start any wallpaper removal, make sure that the old paper on the wall is not the strippable type. With the blade of a utility knife, carefully lift a corner edge of the paper and gently pull it down. Use an even pressure. If the paper is strippable, it will start to peel off the wall with just a little effort on your part. Pull the paper straight down against itself as evenly as possible. When the paper is off, you will notice "fuzz" stuck to the wall surface. Don't sand this off. It provides a base for the new wallpaper. Of course, if you plan to paint the wall rather than paper it, the fuzz should be removed with sandpaper on a sanding block.

If your walls are lath and plaster (not gypsumboard) you may find "hot spots" in the plaster. These are really alkali spots and they are quite common on new plaster walls and some old ones as well. The spots must be treated before you wallpaper or the adhesive won't stick to them.

You may not be able to see the spots by just looking over the surface. Therefore, coat the wall with glue or wall size, as mentioned earlier. The size will cause the hot spots to color so you can see them. Then, neutralize the spots with a mixture of one part 28% acetic acid, and two parts water. We recommend that you wear rubber

gloves and apply the mixture with a soft cloth. Rub the area until the color disappears, which will mean that the alkalis have been dissolved. You may need to go over the surface several times with the acetic acid mixture. When all of the spots have vanished, resize the wall and proceed with the project.

Selection nomenclature

When you shop for wallpaper, the terms "straight patterns" and "dropped patterns" will fly like the adjectives in a politician's campaign speech. "Straight" and "dropped" sound mysterious, but both are very easy to understand.

A "straight" or "straight match" means that the pattern is the same along the roll. The pattern repeats itself horizontally.

A "dropped" or "drop match" means that the design on the bottom or at the end of the roll matches the design on the top of the next roll—and vice versa.

If the design on the paper is directly opposite the design on another roll of the same paper, the

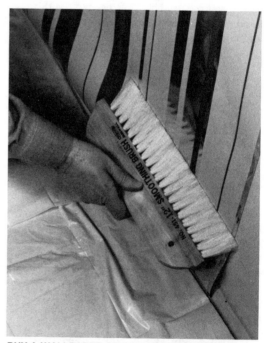

BUY A WALLPAPER SMOOTHING BRUSH. Get the 12-inch size, if possible. As you hang the paper, the bristles of the brush will tend to fill with adhesive. When this occurs, wash out the adhesive with clear water and rub the bristles dry on old toweling. The best way is to have two smoothing brushes. You can put the second one into service while the bristles of the first one dry. Cost of the brushes is nominal.

BUY A WALLPAPER SEAM ROLLER. The roller's surface embeds the wall covering into the adhesive at seams, making a smooth "seam-free" job. Also keep adhesive off the surface of the roller as you work. Use clear water.

FOR STUBBORN SEAMS that won't lie flat and adhere, try using straight pins as clamps until the adhesive dries. The tiny pin holes won't be noticeable when the pins are removed. After the adhesive has set for a time, go back over the seams with the roller once again. Then pin down any seams that won't stick properly. You may have to add extra adhesive behind these spots. Be sure to wipe away excess adhesive as you go.

paper is a straight match. If not, it is, simply, a drop match.

Most wallpaper is pretrimmed; i.e., the edges are trimmed at the factory so they can be butt-joined together. This seam is the easiest to do and looks best because you won't see the double-lapped joints when light strikes the surface a certain way. If the paper has a selvage, it must be trimmed off before the paper is pasted. If you will lap the joints, or seams, only one side of the paper has to be trimmed because the trimmed edge then covers the selvage edge.

A "wire edge" refers to a wallpaper seam that has been lapped about one-sixteenth of an inch. Most paper hangers use the wire edge treatment when they can't butt seam edges perfectly. This usually happens on walls that are not particularly straight and level. A wire edge also is the one to use if the paper is noted to shrink. (Ask the dealer about the shrink factor.) The wire edge allows for this contraction so the seams don't form a gap.

Double cutting is an easy way to get all butted seams to fit perfectly. If you have laid carpeting, you know the term. If not, here's how double cutting works (you will have to add extra wallpaper to your order because of waste):

Paste and hang the wallpaper, lapping the seams. With a straightedge and a very sharp utility knife, cut through both layers of paper—right down into the wall surface. There will be a small strip of paper on the top surface of the cut. Peel this off. Lift the edge of the paper on the wall.

TO PROTECT OUTSIDE CORNERS of wall covering, you can buy a clear corner strip of plastic which is tacked into position. The clear strips are hardly noticeable. The strips come in eight-foot-long units; you cut them with a hacksaw.

You'll see another small strip of paper. Peel this off. Now, butt both edges of paper together. The joint will match perfectly.

Buying a mural takes some planning. First, determine where the mural will go and sketch this wall, noting exact width and height. The mural, which is similar to a large wall painting, will have "borders" at the top, bottom, and edges; i.e., it will fit a specific space. Therefore, furniture placement in the room can be critical. You don't want a sofa, lamp, or table to hide the bottom half of the mural.

If the mural doesn't cover the entire wall space, you will need "background" or, more often, a neutral or unpatterned wallpaper to complete the area. Backgrounds specially made for mural patterns are available.

Murals also are available in designs that can be reduced in size by leaving out a strip or two of the total design, or increased in size by adding strips to fill the wall. Ask the dealer about this when you choose your mural. There could be a cost difference. The same adhesive used for the mural almost always is used for the background paper also. Mildew-resistant adhesive often is specified for both.

Cleaning/protecting paper

Most wallpapers (but not the "standard" ones) can be cleaned by simply sponging them with mild household detergent and water, and then rinsing away the residue. A commercial wallpaper dough also is available. Ease of cleaning can be an important buying decision. Usually manufacturers and dealers tell you how durable and maintenance-free their products are, but nonetheless, before you buy, ask the dealer about care.

As a word of caution, before you wash or clean paper with dough, test it in an area behind a sofa or chair where any mistakes won't show. Also know that cleaning dough can damage the color and texture of the paper. Be careful.

By estimating your wallpaper needs in advance, you will end up with little or no excess paper. Of course, this is what you want to do—but only to a point. It is a good idea to have a little of the wallcovering left over—half a roll or so—and you may want to take this into consideration when figuring your estimates. The reason is this: Somewhere down the line, an area in the paper may become damaged. This spot can be repaired by patching in a new piece (the double-cut process), but you will need the extra paper to match the patch. The aging process of the paper on the wall and the paper in storage will be about the same. Therefore, the patch won't look as new and out of place as would one that you'd make from brand new paper, if indeed you could even find the pattern still in stock.

Some retailers sell protective coatings for some types of wallpaper. The coatings are clear and are brushed or rolled over the paper surface after the wallpapering job is completely dry. The coatings will not discolor the paper. They are especially good for use in high-traffic areas where the paper will be subject to wear, dirt, or grime.

Hanging wallpaper

■ THANKS TO the many ''fabric''-backed wall coverings now available, wallpapering is easier than ever. Since these newer materials come in a wide variety of attractive patterns, they are especially desirable for a first venture.

There are several good reasons. First, these wall coverings are easier to work with than ordinary wallpaper. You can correct mistakes by peeling off strips already in place, without fear of ripping the material. Ordinary wallpaper, once

Tools needed

Carpenter's square

Spirit level

Cutting board,
¾ x 24 x 72-in.

Clean sponge

Yardstick

Stepladder

Plumb line and chalk

Large scissors
or shears

Two plastic buckets
(one for paste and
one for washing)

4-in. brush for
applying paste
(for unpasted
wall covering)

Plastic water tray
(for prepasted
wall covering)

12-in. smoothing
brush

Wall covering
trimmer, utility
knife or single-
edge razor blades

Dropcloth

Corner and seam
rollers

All tools required
for wallpapering
are available at
well-stocked paint
and wall-covering
stores.

How to measure

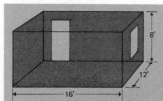

A standard wall-covering roll contains 35 sq. ft.—narrow rolls are longer than wide ones. To allow for waste and matching, figure on covering 30 sq. ft. with each roll.

1. Measure the distance around room at baseboard.

2. Measure wall height from baseboard to ceiling.

3. Find number of rolls you need in chart (right). For example, if room is 8x12x16 ft. with a door and window (as sketched above):

4. Add room dimensions around baseboard:
   12+12+16+16=56 ft.

5. Find 56 in first column of chart.

6. Find number opposite 56 in applicable wall-height column (8 ft.): 14 rolls are needed.

7. Compute square feet of window-door openings and trim, deduct proportionate number of rolls; in this case, deduct one roll for door and window—13 rolls are needed to cover the walls.

8. Before you paper a ceiling, use column at far right to estimate the number of rolls needed—eight in this case.

ROOM ESTIMATING CHART					
Around Room (ft.)	Rolls for Walls in Room With Height of			Border (yds.)	Ceiling (rolls)
	8'	9'	10'		
28	8	8	10	11	2
30	8	8	10	11	2
32	8	10	10	12	2
34	10	10	12	13	4
36	10	10	12	13	4
38	10	12	12	14	4
40	10	12	12	15	4
42	12	12	14	15	4
44	12	12	14	15	4
46	12	14	14	17	6
48	14	14	16	17	6
50	14	14	16	18	6
52	14	14	16	19	6
54	14	16	18	19	6
56	14	16	18	20	8
58	16	16	18	21	8
60	16	18	20	21	8
62	16	18	20	22	8
64	16	18	20	23	8
66	18	20	20	23	10
68	18	20	22	24	10
70	18	20	22	25	10
72	18	20	22	25	12
74	20	22	22	26	12
76	20	22	24	27	12
78	20	22	24	27	14
80	20	22	26	28	14
82	22	24	26	29	14
84	22	24	26	30	16
86	22	24	26	30	16
88	24	26	28	31	16
90	24	26	28	32	18

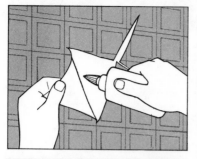

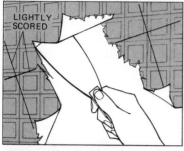

LIGHTLY SCORED

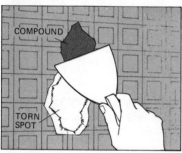

COMPOUND

TORN SPOT

ADHESIVES CHART

	Wheat Paste or Stainless Paste	Liquid Strippable or Wheat Paste	Vinyl Adhesive	Stainless Paste
Regular wallpaper	X			
Strippable wallpaper		X		
Vinyl wall covering			X	
Foils			X	
Burlap with backing			X	
Burlap (porous)	X			
Cork with backing			X	
Silks and fabrics				X
Flocks, murals, hand prints, borders	Use adhesive appropriate for wall covering's backing			

pasted in place, usually cannot be reused. Second, any adhesive on the surface can safely be washed off after the covering is in place.

Finally, wall coverings of the cloth type can be moved in position on the wall until they match perfectly with strips already in place. This maneuverability is extremely limited with ordinary wallpaper.

Types of wall coverings and adhesives

Prepasted wall coverings are popular with do-it-yourselfers because they save time and create considerably less mess. They are available in most of the same designs as unpasted wall coverings.

Unpasted wall coverings offer a slightly greater selection of patterns and finishes, including both flocked and foil coverings. Different types of unpasted wall coverings require different types of adhesive. Use the chart at the right to determine the kind you need.

It is important to mix wheat paste or stainless paste at least one hour before using it. Allowance for this setup time makes it easier to eliminate dry lumps. Properly mixed, the paste will be lump-free and have the consistency of heavy cream.

Dealing with old wallpaper

Don't underestimate the importance of properly preparing the walls to be covered. A professional generally removes an existing covering as there is always the possibility that it may work loose and ruin the new job. If you do cover existing wallpaper, make sure it's tight and smooth.

Cut an X in any air bubble and glue the paper back with white glue. Corners should be cut from floor to ceiling and reglued. Uneven spaces—where paper has pulled off the wall in spots, for example—should be filled with spackling compound and sanded. Check the joints of existing paper, fill with spackling compound and sand smooth where necessary—otherwise they may show through a new covering.

If there are two or more layers of paper on the walls, remove them. The best way is to rent a steamer. It's easy to use and you will have no trouble if you follow instructions. Another way to remove paper is by sponging the walls with hot water and using a scraper. Keep in mind that the wetter the paper, the faster it will come off. When removing paper from drywall, take care not to get under its layer of finish by mistake.

Some extra tips to make the job easier: Before

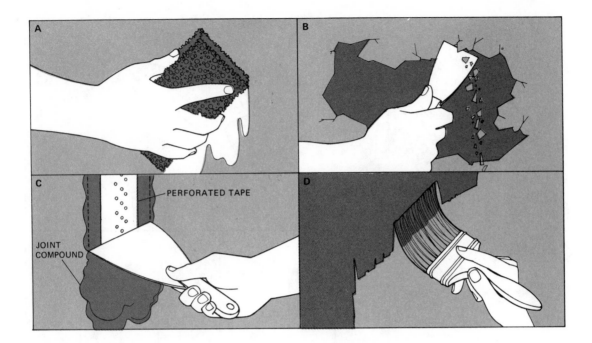

starting the soaking operation, spread many layers of newspaper on the floor—remember that the paper that comes off the wall will have softened glue on the back, which can adhere to the floor, necessitating another soaking and scraping. Lightly score crosshatch marks over the paper with a utility knife (carefully so you don't damage the wall beneath); this will break the surface so that hot water will dissolve the old paste faster.

Preparing plaster and drywall surfaces

On unpainted plaster, make any needed repairs, scrape out loose cracks and fill with spackling compound (joint compound). Then apply a coat of wall size. Painted plaster should be thoroughly washed with detergent and water, rinsed with clear cold water. Make sure no soapy residue is left to dry on the surface. If necessary, remove peeling, chipped or cracked paint with a wide putty or joint knife and sand the surface smooth. Repair cracks or holes with spackling compound, sanding when dry. Dull a gloss or semigloss finish on existing paint with a strong soda solution or coarse-grit sandpaper; slick walls will not satisfactorily accept wall covering adhesives. On new plasterboard, tape seams and apply compound according to maker's directions. Set nailheads without breaking paper (dimple with hammer), cover with compound. Sand surfaces smooth when dry. Use two coats if necessary. Prime walls with oil, alkyd or latex primer-sealer;

with latex, be sure to allow curing time. Sizing surfaces lets you slide covering in position, assures better adhesion.

Switches, fixtures

Before wall covering is applied, all switch plates and outlet covers should be removed and wall fixtures loosened and pulled away from the wall. Remove fixture wall brackets *after turning off power at service panel* and then disconnecting wires. When the wall covering is in place, cut an area slightly smaller than wall plate so that plate covers cutout completely.

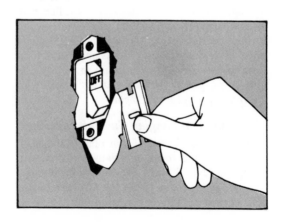

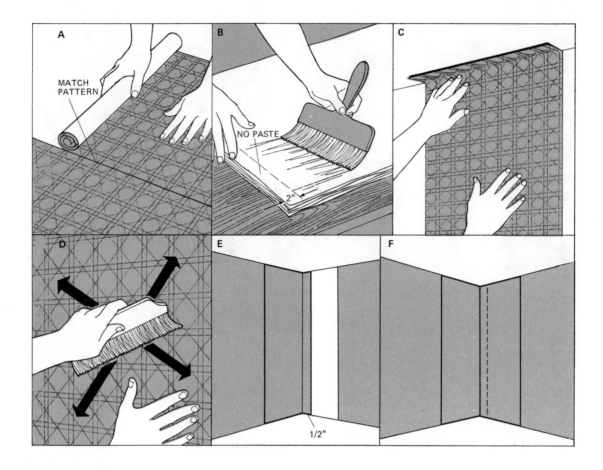

Papering around windows, doors

Doors and windows are handled exactly alike, except that a window means extra wall to be covered below it. Make a rough cutout by measuring from the last strip to the window casing and add ½ in. Measure the same way from ceiling and baseboard to trim. Remove the cutout before applying paste. Hang the strip, press in around casing and roll the joint with the seam roller; trim excess paper. Measure cutout size for the second strip as for the first and hang it, butting the first strip, in the same manner. Press and roll at joint with casing; trim. If you have taken care in cutting strips, pattern-matching at doors and windows will present no problem.

Preparing and hanging the wall covering

Two rules of thumb: If you plan to paper all the way around the room, hang the first strip along the edge of a door or window. If there is a fireplace in the room, center the first strip over it and work in both directions from there.

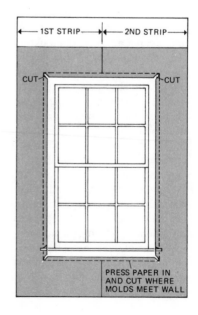

On an ample-sized table—a 2 x 6-ft. piece of ¾-in. plywood on sawhorses is fine—unroll the wall covering and lay it face up. Measure out wall height and add 6 in. allowance to trim. Lay the second strip next to the first, match the pattern and cut it to the same length. Lay the second strip on top of the first and continue matching and cutting strips in this manner.

When all strips are cut, turn over the stack of paper. Apply adhesive evenly with a large paste brush. Start at the center and brush toward the bottom. For easier handling, leave a 1-in. strip at the bottom unpasted. Allow about three minutes for the paper to expand before you handle it. Now fold the bottom half of the strip toward the center, paste to paste, without creasing the paper. Stop short of the center so that the fold you later make from the top will be slightly longer than the bottom one. Align the edges carefully. Apply paste to the top half of the strip as to the bottom, wait for paper to expand, and fold the top over to the center. The 1 in. unpasted strip at the top should overlap the bottom edge folded up to the center.

To hang the paper, unfold the top section and place the strip high on the wall, overlapping the ceiling-wall joint by approximately 2 in., and aligning its edge with a vertical snapped with your chalked plumb line. Give the upper section a couple of strokes with your smoothing brush to hold it to the wall. Then open the lower section. When you are satisfied with the paper's alignment, brush the entire strip smooth. Always brush from the center toward edges to get rid of air bubbles. Trim off excess paper at baseboard and ceiling joint and around doors and windows.

To hang the second strip, use the first as a guide, matching the pattern and butting—not overlapping—the seams. Repeat the smoothing procedure, then roll the seam with the seam roller. On flocked or embossed wall covering, seams should not be rolled—instead, tap along the seam with the tips of the smoothing-brush bristles. Clean strips with a damp sponge immediately to remove any paste on the surface, ceiling or baseboard. Hang remaining strips the same way.

To prepare a corner, measure from the last strip to the corner at ceiling level, midpoint and baseboard. Add ½ in. to the widest measurement, cut a strip to this width, and hang it in the usual manner; it will overlap the corner by ½ in. Snap a plumb chalkline over this overlap for use as a guide in hanging the first strip on the other wall of the corner. This technique will give you a true vertical even if the corner is not perfectly straight.

Country weather vanes

■ WEATHER VANES WERE A COMMON sight on the landscape of early America. Not only did they prepare our agrarian ancestors for changes in atmospheric conditions, but weather vane construction served as a creative occupation during long winter evenings.

All vanes shown are display replicas created of either wood, metal or both.

Running stag

Although the running stag is made of wood, it is skillfully painted to look as if it's covered with verdigris, the greenish-blue substance that forms on copper, brass and bronze. Since all authentic weather vanes are covered with verdigris, creating the greenish cast on the running stag assures its authentic appearance.

Before you begin your work, read the instructions through and round up all tools and materials you'll need. Use clear pine for the project.

Draw patterns. To draw the stag, lay out a full-size grid on ¾-in. clear pine; draw each square 2 × 2 in. Sketch the stag pattern, following the drawing. Draw the grid and transfer the antler pattern onto ¼-in. stock.

1 RUNNING STAG is typical of country weather vanes fashioned by early craftsmen. This one is of wood and finished to simulate look of old copper.

2 PUFFING STEAM LOCOMOTIVE recalls an earlier era. Constructed of sheet metal painted black, it is mounted on a hardwood base shaped like railroad tracks.

3 THE AMERICA, patterned after a gaff-rigged Colonial sloop, is of wood with metal sails. The original boats of this type were used for pilot and fishing boats.

4 THE INDIAN STALKING A BEAR can be hung on the wall. The figures are of wood inserted into a metal U-channel ad underscored by an arrow carved of wood.

Making the stag. Carefully cut out the stag body with a scroll or band saw. Or rought-cut it with a sabre saw and finish-shape with a Surform tool. Following the drawing and the photo, use rasps and a whittling knife to shape the stag body (edges) realistically. A handheld grinder is very helpful. Sand the work smooth with medium-grit (80) sandpaper; however, don't sand away the detail.

Distress the stag in the following way to ensure an antique appearance. Tap at random with the ball end of a ball-peen hammer. Test on scrap wood to determine the amount of force required to make a smooth dent. The marks should be distinct. Use care on the tail and legs to avoid breaking them. Use an icepick or awl to add some "bullet holes" like those found on many antique vanes.

Shaping the antlers. It's easiest to shape the antlers with a hand grinder, but you can use a whittling knife if you prefer. Alternate the direction of the antler tips to get a three-dimensional effect (when viewed from the front). Shape the bottom of the antlers into a flat, angled pad. Counterbore for a No. 6 flathead screw. Cut a $\frac{1}{16}$-in. mortise into the head where the antlers attach.

Bore pilot holes in the head for screws to attach the antlers. Set the antlers aside.

Cutting the base. To make the base, first cut the two wood pieces that form the roof. Nail them together with 4d common nails. The ball resting on top of a rectangular base is carved from a single piece of 4 × 4. You can substitute a ready-made gate post finial if you prefer.

Before you shape the ball, bore the hole for the metal rod holding the stag. Then mark off the ball area. You may want to round off the edges and corners with a sabre saw before shaping the ball with a whittling knife or carving tools. Or you can turn the ball and rectangle from a single block of 4 × 4 stock. Shape the ball on the lathe, remove stock from the lathe and shape the rectangular base, using saw and hand tools. Then cut a 90° V-shape into the bottom of the rectangle to fit it over the roof.

Cut a $\frac{3}{8}$-in.-dia. × 8$\frac{3}{4}$-in. metal rod. Position the rod vertically under the stag so it touches the stag's front hoof. Bore a hole for the rod in the stag.

Cut a $\frac{3}{4}$-in.-dia. × 20-in. dowel with tapered ends according to the drawing. Bore a $\frac{3}{8}$-in. dia. hole in the dowel for the metal rod. Secure the dowel to the metal rod with epoxy adhesive; se-

cure the dowel to the stag's hind hoof with white glue.

Painting the stag. Apply the paint with a brush except as noted. First, paint only the roof with flat black paint. Apply two coats.

The metal rod, wood dowel, ears and antlers are painted with the same color mixture: a black-green-bronze mix of flat black, yellow and hunter green. Daub the paint over the entire surface with a "sponge" of Turkish towel wadded into a ball.

Immediately after you apply the paint, add a little more yellow and green to lighten the mix. Blend this lighter color on about 80 percent of the antlers, dowel and rod for variation. The tips should be lighter than the rest of the antler. When they are partially dry, rub with steel wool through the paint on the edges and tips back to the wood to create a bone effect.

To finish the stag and the ball, spray three coats of copper metallic paint or enough to make a shiny surface. Let the paint dry thoroughly after the third coat.

Apply artificial beads of "solder" at the neck, tail base and points where the legs join the body, using a tube of plastic aluminum repair material. This gives the appearance of metal seams. Let this dry for about 10 minutes.

Mix some water putty to a thick consistency. Apply it to the stag and ball, completely covering the metallic color but not filling in the details. Set the pieces aside for several hours until thoroughly dry.

Attach the ball to the roof and install the stag on the finial.

Mix a flat dull yellow-green mixture using flat white as the base with smaller amounts of hunter green, sunset yellow, and touches of black and royal blue. Look at a piece of weathered copper, if available, to get an idea of the shade. Brush the greenish mixture over the stag and the finial.

While the paint is still wet, dip the same brush or rag into a bit of flat black paint and lightly into a thinner such as turpentine. Touch the stag along the top edge across the body, tail, top edge of the legs and head, allowing the thinned paint mix to run down through the wet green mixture. Don't try to touch up the runs. If too much black appears for your taste, quickly apply a little clear thinner at the top edge.

The dull black discoloration often appears on the under edges, under the jaw line, crotch, knee bend and at the lower edges of the solder seams. The results should leave some of the green mix-

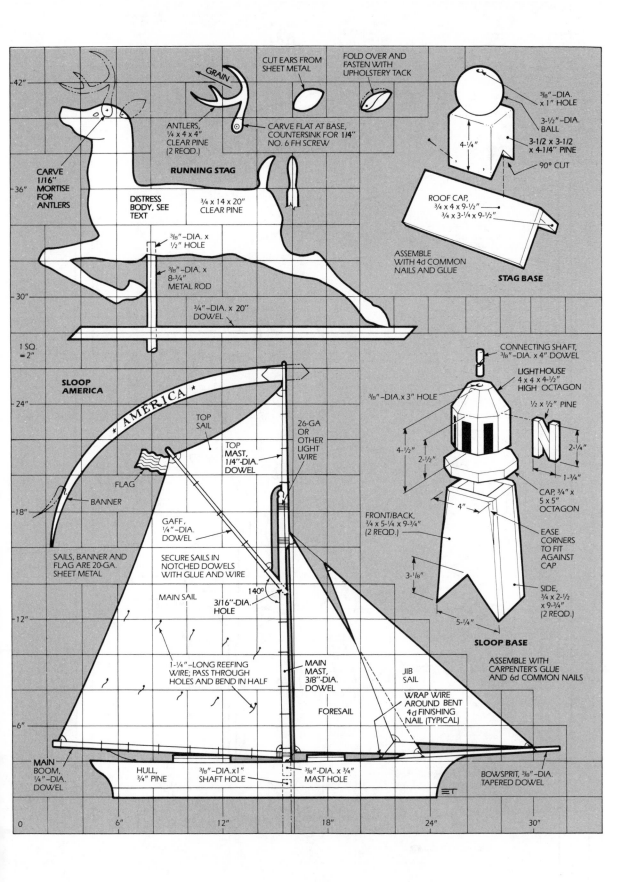

CUT EARS FROM SHEET METAL

FOLD OVER AND FASTEN WITH UPHOLSTERY TACK

GRAIN

ANTLERS, ¼ x 4 x 4" CLEAR PINE (2 REQD.)

CARVE FLAT AT BASE, COUNTERSINK FOR ¼" NO. 6 FH SCREW

RUNNING STAG

CARVE 1/16" MORTISE FOR ANTLERS

DISTRESS BODY, SEE TEXT

¾ x 14 x 20" CLEAR PINE

⅜"-DIA. x ½" HOLE

⅜"-DIA. x 8-¾" METAL ROD

¾"-DIA. x 20" DOWEL

42"

36"

30"

1 SQ. = 2"

⅜"-DIA. x 1" HOLE

3-½"-DIA. BALL

3-½ x 3-½ x 4-¼" PINE

4-¼"

90° CUT

ROOF CAP, ¾ x 4 x 9-½" ¾ x 3-¼ x 9-½"

ASSEMBLE WITH 4d COMMON NAILS AND GLUE

STAG BASE

SLOOP AMERICA

AMERICA

24"

TOP SAIL

TOP MAST, ¼"-DIA. DOWEL

26-GA OR OTHER LIGHT WIRE

FLAG

BANNER

18"

GAFF, ¼"-DIA. DOWEL

SAILS, BANNER AND FLAG ARE 20-GA. SHEET METAL

SECURE SAILS IN NOTCHED DOWELS WITH GLUE AND WIRE

MAIN SAIL

140°

3/16"-DIA. HOLE

12"

1-¼"-LONG REEFING WIRE; PASS THROUGH HOLES AND BEND IN HALF

MAIN MAST, ⅜"-DIA. DOWEL

JIB SAIL

FORESAIL

WRAP WIRE AROUND BENT 4d FINISHING NAIL (TYPICAL)

6"

MAIN BOOM, ¼"-DIA. DOWEL

HULL, ¾" PINE

⅜"-DIA. x 1" SHAFT HOLE

⅜"-DIA. x ¾" MAST HOLE

BOWSPRIT, ⅜"-DIA. TAPERED DOWEL

CONNECTING SHAFT, ⅜"-DIA. x 4" DOWEL

LIGHT HOUSE 4 x 4 x 4-½" HIGH OCTAGON

⅜"-DIA. x 3" HOLE

½ x ½" PINE

4-½"

2-½"

2-¼"

1-¾"

FRONT/BACK, ¾ x 5-¼ x 9-¾" (2 REQD.)

4"

CAP, ¾" x 5 x 5" OCTAGON

EASE CORNERS TO FIT AGAINST CAP

3-⅛"

SIDE, ¾ x 2-½ x 9-¾" (2 REQD.)

5-¼"

SLOOP BASE

ASSEMBLE WITH CARPENTER'S GLUE AND 6d COMMON NAILS

0   6"   12"   18"   24"   30"

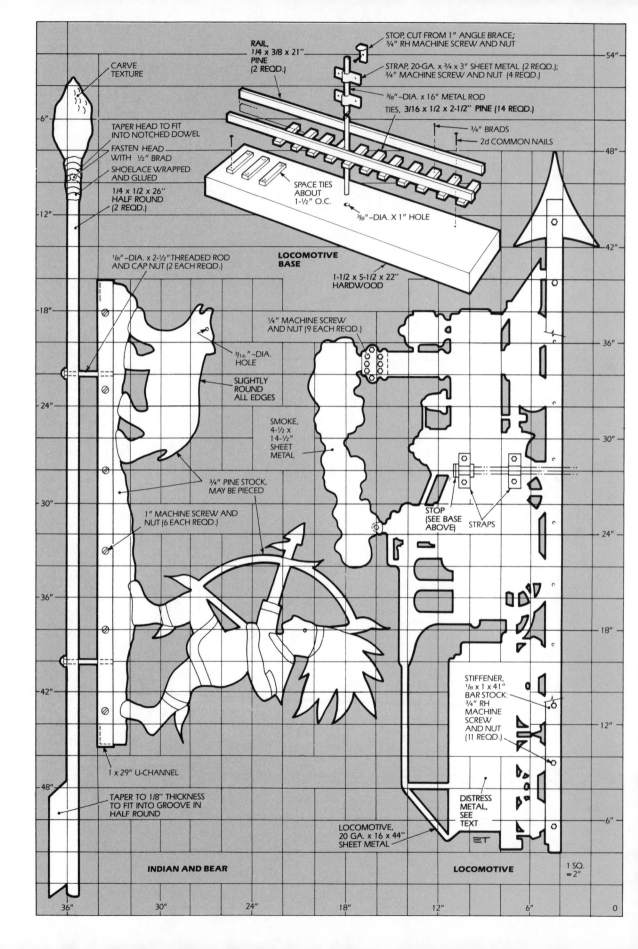

CARVE TEXTURE

RAIL, 1/4 x 3/8 x 21" PINE (2 REQD.)

STOP, CUT FROM 1" ANGLE BRACE; 3/4" RH MACHINE SCREW AND NUT

STRAP, 20-GA. x 3/4 x 3" SHEET METAL (2 REQD.); 3/4" MACHINE SCREW AND NUT (4 REQD.)

3/8"-DIA. x 16" METAL ROD

TIES, 3/16 x 1/2 x 2-1/2" PINE (14 REQD.)

TAPER HEAD TO FIT INTO NOTCHED DOWEL

FASTEN HEAD WITH 1/2" BRAD

SHOELACE WRAPPED AND GLUED

1/4 x 1/2 x 26" HALF ROUND (2 REQD.)

3/4" BRADS

2d COMMON NAILS

SPACE TIES ABOUT 1-1/2" O.C.

3/8"-DIA. X 1" HOLE

LOCOMOTIVE BASE

1-1/2 x 5-1/2 x 22" HARDWOOD

1/8"-DIA. x 2-1/2" THREADED ROD AND CAP NUT (2 EACH REQD.)

1/4" MACHINE SCREW AND NUT (9 EACH REQD.)

3/16"-DIA. HOLE

SLIGHTLY ROUND ALL EDGES

SMOKE, 4-1/2 x 14-1/2" SHEET METAL

3/4" PINE STOCK, MAY BE PIECED

STOP (SEE BASE ABOVE)

STRAPS

1" MACHINE SCREW AND NUT (6 EACH REQD.)

STIFFENER, 1/8 x 1 x 41" BAR STOCK; 3/4" RH MACHINE SCREW AND NUT (11 REQD.)

1 x 29" U-CHANNEL

DISTRESS METAL, SEE TEXT

TAPER TO 1/8" THICKNESS TO FIT INTO GROOVE IN HALF ROUND

LOCOMOTIVE, 20 GA. x 16 x 44" SHEET METAL

INDIAN AND BEAR

LOCOMOTIVE

1 SQ. = 2"

36"   30"   24"   18"   12"   6"   0

ture with light black "rain" marks and some whitish water putty showing through. The thinner should drip down on the roof as well.

Let the stag dry for several minutes. Then hold a toothbrush dipped in black at a 60° angle to the stag, push the bristles back with your finger and let them splatter the stag. Do this only once on each side. Let the paint dry thoroughly.

Finally, if desired, use triple-0 steel wool to reveal tiny amounts of copper at the hoof edges, tail tip and ridge of the nose. Also use steel wool to reveal the solder seams.

Secure the antlers with screws. Then fold the metal ears and attach them with an upholstery tack.

Locomotive

You can make the locomotive of metal roof flashing. It's commonly available at lumberyards and home centers.

Draw a grid of 2-in. squares on paper. Following the pattern, pencil in the locomotive outline. When you are satisfied, cut out the pattern. Tape it on the flashing and scribe around it with a nail. The smoke is a separate piece of metal attached by machine screws.

Cut out the metal. First, clear metal away from the corners and other tight places with a drill. Then use a sharpened steel chisel, a scroll saw or a jeweler's saw to cut the lines.

File away the burrs, leaving some of the roughness for a hand-crafted appearance. Flatten the metal by laying it on a concrete surface and pounding the edges with a mallet or hammer. Go over the surface lightly, tapping to create slight dents to add to the antique appearance.

Cut the bar stock to length and position it on the lower edge of the locomotive. Mark and drill through both pieces of metal for the machine screws. Installing one machine screw before making the remaining holes will avoid offset holes.

Make the stop for the vertical rod from a 11-in. angle brace. Cut off ½-in. from one side. This should remove any holes on that side. Use a file to round off the corners. Drill and attach the angle brace.

Cut two sheet-metal straps to hold the rod in place. Rest the rod on the work surface and shape the straps over the rod with a hammer or mallet. Use a chisel to form a clean angle at the point where the strap meets the locomotive surface.

Position the rod against the angle brace. Use a square along the edge of the bar stock to be sure the rod is perpendicular. Position the straps and bore or punch holes with a nail for the machine

screws. Drill holes and secure the smoke in place with machine screws.

Constructing the base. To give weight to the base, a scrap piece of butcher block or any piece of dense hardwood will do the job. If you use lighter pine, enlarge the base to support the vane.

Cut the base to size and round all edges lightly with a rasp. You can distress the base by striking the visible sides flat against a rough concrete surface.

Use a drill press or drill guide with your portable drill to bore a plumb hole centered on the block for the rod. Test-position the vane and rod to assure stability before proceeding.

Cut enough railroad ties to cover the length of the base. Place them 1½ in. on center. Cut rails and round their top edges with sandpaper. Lay the rails inside the nailheads on the ties.

Finishing the locomotive. Brush two complete coats of metal primer over the train, rod and base. Apply the second coat as soon as the first is set enough not to lift. Lightly brush away runs or drips on the surface. Leave drips and beads of paint along the edges. Do not leave runs on the surface.

When the primer is set enough so it won't lift (about one hour), apply two heavy coats of flat black paint in the same way you applied the primer. Let the paint dry thoroughly—about 48 hours.

To achieve a weathered look, apply the following techniques sparingly: Use a wooden spoon or wooden stick to knock off beads of paint. Strike the edges and machine screws to reveal some prime coat. When dry, wash the piece with detergent. Test a spot using a strong cleaner and a scrub brush. Dust wood ashes on and wipe them off to achieve a "patina." Bend the points of the arrowhead and straighten them so a crease is visible.

Sloop America

The sloop *America* has a ¾-in. pine hull, dowel masts and booms, and sails made of roof flashing or other sheet metal.

Begin work by drawing a grid of 2-in. squares directly onto the pine stock and sketching in the hull. Cut out the hull and the two cabins. Then carve the bow and stern shapes with a hand grinder or a whittling knife. Sand the parts smooth with 80-grit abrasive.

Use a drill press to bore the mast and shaft holes according to the drawing. The holes line up, but do not bore through the wood; make separate holes.

Drive 4d finishing nails into the hull as shown in the drawing. Bend the nails over so you can attach sail wires to them later.

Making the masts. Cut the main mast dowel. Shape the ball on top. The gaff fits into an angled hole in the mainmast. To bore the hole, insert the down in a V-block holder made of scrap wood. Bore the hole on a drill press. Glue the mast in place with white glue.

Cut the top mast. Taper it to shape at the top and cut away the surface next to the main mast for a flush fit. Carefully cut a 1/16-in. notch in the top mast to fit the topsail.

Glue the top mast in place. Wrap the masts together with 26-ga. or other light wire and tuck in the loose ends neatly. Embed the end of the wire in glue; wipe off excess glue.

Cut the main boom. Attach it to the main mast with wire as shown in the drawing.

Cut the gaff and taper the free end. Reduce to 3/16-in.-dia. the end that is inserted in the main mast.

Cut the bowsprit, taper its free end and shape the other end according to the drawing. Bore a 1/16-in.-dia. pilot hole, then glue and nail the bowsprit in place with a 4d finishing nail.

Shaping the sails. On paper, carefully draw a grid of 2-in. squares to use in enlarging the four sails and the *America* banner patterns. Sketch in the sails and banner, then cut out the patterns. The flag and mainsail are one piece.

Tape the patterns to sheet metal, scribe around them with a sharp nail and cut out the sails and the banner. Use a sharpened steel chisel, a scroll saw or a jeweler's saw.

File away the burrs. Flatten the metal if needed by laying it on a concrete surface and pounding the edges with a mallet or hammer.

Create ripples in the flag by tapping with a mallet or hammer over a 6d finishing nail. You might try this on scrap metal first to get the feel and master the technique. Shape the furl in the banner by bending the metal with needlenose pliers.

Fastening the sails. Begin securing the sails to the masts and booms. First bore holes in the mainsail for the reefing wire and wire to attach the sail to the gaff, main boom and main mast. Use a sharp nail to make the holes.

Attach the mainsail to the main mast with wire loops. Cut oversize wire lengths, feed them through the sail, twist them snugly to the mast to secure the sail, then cut the wire close to the loop.

Attach the mainsail to the main boom in the same manner. Leave it free of the gaff.

Bore attachment holes in the topsail. For the moment, attach the topsail to the top mast with a single loop of wire at the top. Attach the gaff to the top and main sails with one wire running through both sails and around the gaff. Attach the remaining wires to the top mast.

Attach the mainsail wire from the main boom to a 4d finishing nail bent over behind the aft cabin.

Bore attachment holes in the jib. Using the jib to locate the spot, bore a hole through the top mast for a wire to secure the jib. Fit the wire through the top of the jib and secure it temporarily with a small twist.

Thread the loose end through the mast and leave it unsecured for now. Wire the lower rear foot of the jib to a bent 4d finishing nail at the bottom of the mast. Bore under the bowsprit to attach wire to the forward foot of the jib. Secure the wire. Bore three attachment holes in the foresail and secure it in place with wires.

Attach the banner by wrapping it around the top mast and tapping it with a mallet to form a collar. Wrap the banner so the tabs fold across the back side.

The banner should swing freely on the mast; it is removed for painting. Feed reefing wires through the mainsail and flatten them against the wall.

Constructing the base. The sloop base is a lighthouse that rests on a stand with an octagonal cap. Lay out and cut the front and back of the stand, make the V-grooves and ease the top corners. Cut the stand sides. Glue and nail parts together with 4d common nails. Lay out and cut the lighthouse from a 4 × 4. Use a drill press to bore a 3/8-in.-dia. hole for the shaft. Nail the cap to the bottom of the lighthouse. Place this assembly on the stand and nail through the cap.

Cut the pieces for the "N," which designates North. Glue the parts together. After the glue has set, glue the N to the lighthouse and temporarily tape it in place. cut the connecting dowel.

• *Finishing the sloop.* Brush two coats of flat white over the entire weather vane, including the base. The paint should fill the space around the wires and nails; however, don't let it run. Let the paint dry overnight.

Next, remove the banner and paint it. Paint the ground first and let it dry. Ground is regal red, the lettering and stars are sunset yellow and there are touches of black.

Begin from the top and paint the sloop: First paint the flag with regal red and royal blue. Then paint the sails a sand color. The hull is gloss black, the cabin sides are hunter green and the cabin tops are gloss black. Let the hull dry before painting the waterline regal red. Add other touches of color.

Indian and bear

The Indian and bear weather vane is made of ¾-in. pine stock. Its features are carved in low relief.

Begin work by drawing a full-size grid of 2-in. squares on cardboard. Draw in the Indian and the bear with the ground underneath them, the arrowhead and the feather. Cut out the patterns and trace them onto wood.

Cut out the designs with a scroll or band saw. Or rough-cut the figures with a sabre saw and finish with a coping saw.

Use a whittling knife, carving tools or a hand grinder to shape the headdress and to cut low reliefs into the surface to outline the details. It is easier to handle the pieces if you separate the bear and the Indian.

In shaping the headdress, start with the front feather, after the plume at the top of the bow. Round it off in an arc to the right. Then carve out a slight concave shape to create the appearance of the feather bending. Carve as much or as little as suits you. Repeat down the headdress, shaping the tips in alternating directions.

The rest of the carving on the piece is low relief. For example, the headband rests *over* both the headdress feathers and the head. Therefore, carve the feathers and the head slightly down to meet the headband; shear-cut the headband to meet the feathers and the head. The same applies to the neck band, arm and leg.

Carve the plumes at the legs and on the bow to a point. Cut in at the base to form the plume shape.

Carve the arrowhead to a point. Round and smooth with 80-grit abrasive all the uncarved outer edges on the pieces. Simply round and smooth the bear.

Mark and bore holes for the eyes of both the bear and the Indian. Mount the two in U-channel stock. Drill and set machine screws. Installing one machine screw before proceeding will avoid offset holes.

Carving the arrow. Carve the large arrowhead to a sharp edge all around. Cut concave shapes into the surface. The "cutting" edge of the arrowhead should follow the midline of the material.

Whittle the tail of the arrowhead down to ⅛-in. width to fit between two pieces of half-round molding that form the arrow shaft. Whittle a fin along the top edge of the tail feather to ⅛ × ½ in. deep. It will fit between the two pieces of half-round. Then cut the molding to size.

Shape the lower part of the tail feather to a thin edge. Glue the flat surfaces of the half-rounds with white glue; clamp together lightly in the center. Quickly slip the arrowhead and tail feather in place. If necessary, carefully tack-nail the parts.

Coat a shoelace with glue and wrap it tightly around the shaft at the base of the arrowhead. Wrapping should be slightly irregular. The last wrapping should crisscross on one side. Use a pocket knife or other tool to slip the loose end of the lace under one of the wrappings. Wipe off any excess glue. An additional clamp behind the shoelace may be required to close the shaft. Set the arrow aside to dry.

Bore two holes through the channel into wood for ⅛-in.-dia. threaded rods that attach the arrow. Lay the arrow in place next to the channel and mark for the two ⅛-in.—dia. rod holes. Drilling will be through the glue joint, so be sure the glue is dry and the arrow is stable.

Thread the ⅛-in. rods up through the arrow shaft into the base of the vane. Fit plain or capnuts on the rod ends. Once they're in place, lightly file the threads smooth.

• *Finishing the piece.* Use three colors of oil paints on the weather vane: flat black, flat white and terra cotta.

Brush terra cotta onto the face, arms and upper legs of the Indian and on the ground and arrow shaft. Apply white to the headdress feather, tunic body, leggings, plumes and arrowhead wrappings. Tips of the headdress feathers, headband, tunic trim, bow, bowstring, legging trim, arrowhead and bear base are black.

The paint should fully cover the area you are working on so that no wood grain or knots show. Apply several coats of each paint. Wait an hour between each coat until the paint sets. Let the entire project dry for 48 hours after the last coat is applied. Carefully tone down the white if desired by wiping with fireplace ashes.

Colonial weather station

■ THIS WEATHER STATION not only makes an attractive wall decoration for den or family room; it keeps you posted on relative humidity, temperature and barometric pressure 24 hours a day. The eagle and instrument plaques are cut from knot-free (clear) white pine. To simplify cutting and working the small plaques, gang the three in a row and cut them apart after making the holes and boring the corners.

Holding small pieces for shaping is difficult, especially when the work is smaller than the router base. To do this simply and safely, make a workholder by driving a few brads up through the bottom of a piece of ¼-in. plywood and clamp or nail this to the workbench. The work is simply pressed down on the protruding brads.

Humidity and temperature gauges are merely press-fitted into their holes. A separate flange is provided to hold the barometer bezel. This is pressed over the flange after it is screwed in place.

Since weather instruments must "breathe," wood spacers are glued to the backs. Tiny screweyes and brass chain link the plaques.

You can finish the wood parts as desired; the antique colors are ideal for pine.

INSTRUMENTS ARE HELD in panels by a snug press-fit. The holes can be sawed, or bored on a drill press.

HOLDING WORK when shaping edge is made easy by resting it on brad points driven up through plywood.

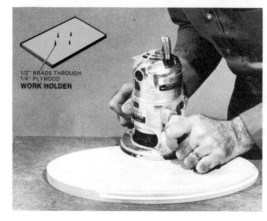

SAWING HOLES for instruments is less of a problem when the three panels are sawed as one, then cut apart.

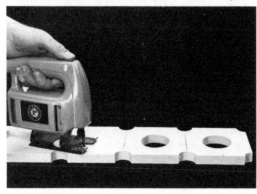

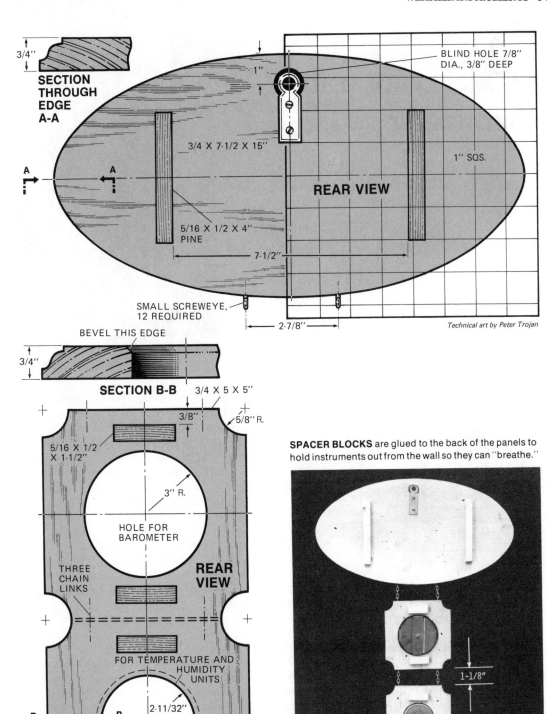

SECTION
THROUGH
EDGE
A-A

3/4"

BLIND HOLE 7/8"
DIA., 3/8" DEEP

1"

A ← → A

3/4 X 7-1/2 X 15"

REAR VIEW

1" SQS.

5/16 X 1/2 X 4"
PINE

7-1/2"

SMALL SCREWEYE,
12 REQUIRED

2-7/8"

Technical art by Peter Trojan

3/4"

BEVEL THIS EDGE

SECTION B-B

3/4 X 5 X 5"

3/8"

5/8" R.

5/16 X 1/2
X 1-1/2"

3" R.

HOLE FOR
BAROMETER

THREE
CHAIN
LINKS

REAR
VIEW

FOR TEMPERATURE AND
HUMIDITY
UNITS

2-11/32"
R.

B ← → B

SPACER BLOCKS are glued to the back of the panels to
hold instruments out from the wall so they can "breathe."

1-1/8"

Accurate water barometer

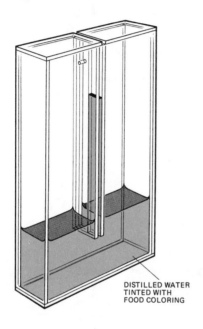

DISTILLED WATER
TINTED WITH
FOOD COLORING

■ BAROMETRIC PRESSURE can be measured by a variety of devices. A most ingenious—and simple—one to make is the water barometer. It is surprisingly accurate in predicting stormy weather by the rise of the water level in its spout.

In this barometer, a high water level in the spout corresponds to a low-pressure system and vice versa. Being sensitive to temperature changes and atmospheric pressure, it should be placed where room temperature is fairly constant—not in direct sunlight.

Except for the walnut mounting panel, it is made almost entirely of ⅛-in. sheet acrylic plastic. The three pieces for the internal U-shaped spout are cut and cemented together first. Here it's best to use a fourth (scrap) piece as a temporary spacer between the two sides to keep them

parallel. Hold the four pieces together with one hand and apply the cement to the back edges of the three with the other. See that the cement does not reach the temporary spacer and prevent it from being removed when cement is dry. A ⁷/₆₄-in. hole must be made in the glued-up assembly to insure equal pressure in both chambers of the barometer.

The spout is centered and cemented, first to the 4 x 7¼-in. back member, then to the front, ⅛-in. from the top. Tabs of masking tape will help you hold the spout in position. See that there are no air leaks along cemented edges. If a leak is found, a drop or two of epoxy glue will seal it.

All other pieces, except the mounting post, are 1 in. wide, and to insure uniformity and a perfect fit, it's best to cut the five parts from a single inch-wide strip of plastic. Sanding and buffing, necessary only where edges are exposed, should be done before the parts are cemented. Start with medium-grit abrasive paper, then use fine and, finally, very fine grit before polishing with a cloth buffing wheel charged with jeweler's rouge. Cement the two 1 x 7¼-in. side pieces to the front and back members first, inserting them between the two and flush with the edges. Then cement the 1 x 4¼-in. bottom piece, using masking tape to hold it, followed by the two top pieces. Top and bottom pieces lap the edges; only the sides fit between.

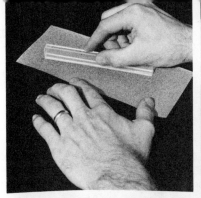
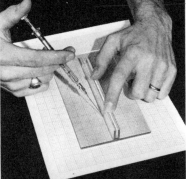
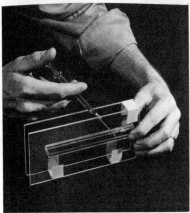
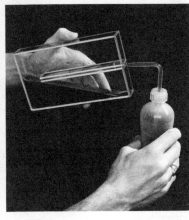

SANDING and polishing of the edges is required only when they are exposed. Start with a medium paper and work up to a very fine grade.

A SPECIAL cement applicator, or syringe, is used to "weld" parts together by capillary action. Avoid getting cement on the surface.

MASKING TAPE is used to hold the parts in alignment while they are being cemented. It's important that the joints do not leak air.

FILLING with distilled water tinted with food coloring is best done with a chemist's wash bottle or a clean plastic squeeze bottle.

Now check for leaks by filling the barometer with water; use epoxy to seal any holes. A ¼-in.-sq. plastic post is used to mount the barometer to the walnut panel. Before cementing it to the back of the barometer, drill and tap two holes in it for 6-32 x ¼-in. rh machine screws. The section view, at right, shows how screws fit in counterbored holes in the back of the mounting panel.

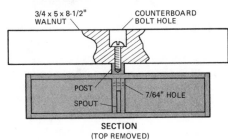

3/4 x 5 x 8-1/2" WALNUT
COUNTERBOARD BOLT HOLE
POST
SPOUT
7/64" HOLE

SECTION
(TOP REMOVED)

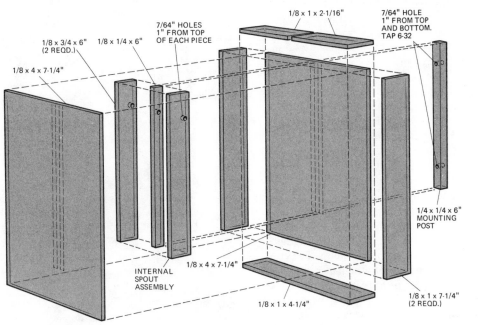

1/8 x 3/4 x 6" (2 REQD.)
1/8 x 1/4 x 6"
7/64" HOLES 1" FROM TOP OF EACH PIECE
1/8 x 1 x 2-1/16"
7/64" HOLE 1" FROM TOP AND BOTTOM. TAP 6-32
1/8 x 4 x 7-1/4"
1/4 x 1/4 x 6" MOUNTING POST
INTERNAL SPOUT ASSEMBLY
1/8 x 4 x 7-1/4"
1/8 x 1 x 4-1/4"
1/8 x 1 x 7-1/4" (2 REQD.)

Banjo barometer

■ IN EARLIER DAYS householders relied on barometers for daily weather "reports." These instruments were generally of the "banjo" type and many were made both large and ornate. By using less complicated and relatively inexpensive instrumentation, you can make a banjo barometer which is an ornamental and useful replica of the older types.

The barometer illustrated has all the fittings of the old ones except the level, which is unnecessary when an aneroid-type instrument is used. The frame, cap and pediment are of mahogany. Select a choice piece with attractive grain for the frame, enlarge and trace the pattern on it and then saw just outside the pattern lines so that you have a little stock left for sanding to profile.

Before you bore or saw the openings for the barometer and hygrometer, have the instruments at hand and determine from them the size of the openings. Allow a little extra for clearance, about ⅛ in. all around. Be sure also that the holes are located on the center line of the frame. The same will be true of the boxed thermometer, the oval-shaped "shell" inlay and the mirror. Overall dimensions given for the oval-shaped inlay are only approximations; they may vary so have the inlay at hand to lay out the recess.

Screws will be furnished with the fittings for attaching the mirror, the barometer and the hygrometer but not always for the thermometer. Use No. 0 ½-in. roundhead screws to attach the latter. Don't take the inside dimensions of the thermometer box literally. Check the size of the thermometer before you make the box, just to be sure there are no variations.

Don't hurry the sanding of the frame, particularly the bandsawed edges. Here you'll want to remove every saw mark by careful and thorough sanding to assure a flawless finish. The corners will require sanding with the paper wrapped around a dowel. Work progressively finer grades, finishing up with 180-grit garnet paper. A cabinet scraper will help remove saw marks fast.

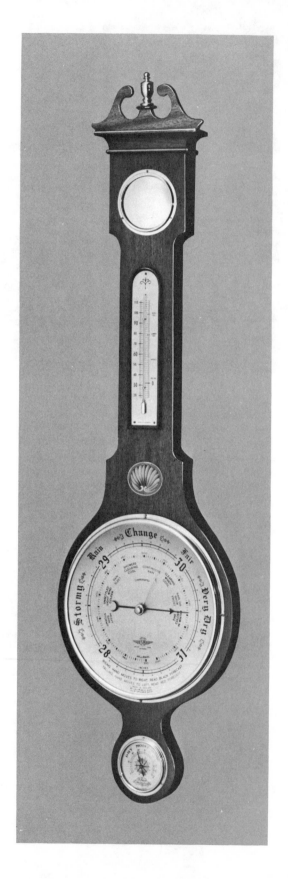

THE PEDIMENT PATTERN is traced on ¼-in. mahogany plywood. Place it so grain runs horizontally.

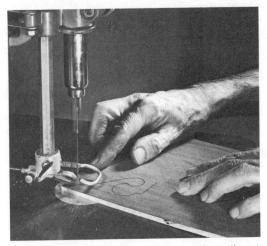

A JIGSAW does the best job of sawing out the pediment. Use a fine blade and follow the line carefully.

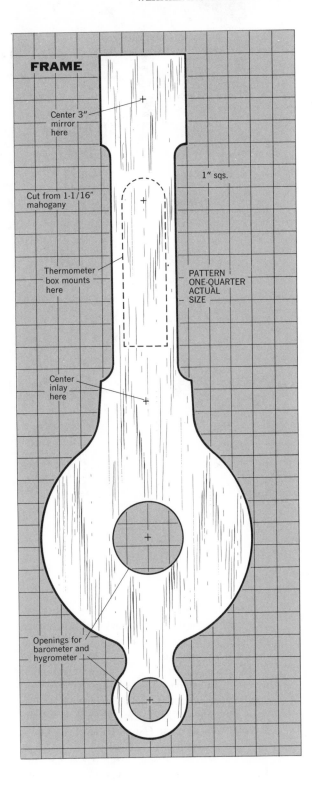

FRAME

Center 3" mirror here

Cut from 1-1/16" mahogany

Thermometer box mounts here

Center inlay here

Openings for barometer and hygrometer

1" sqs.

PATTERN ONE-QUARTER ACTUAL SIZE

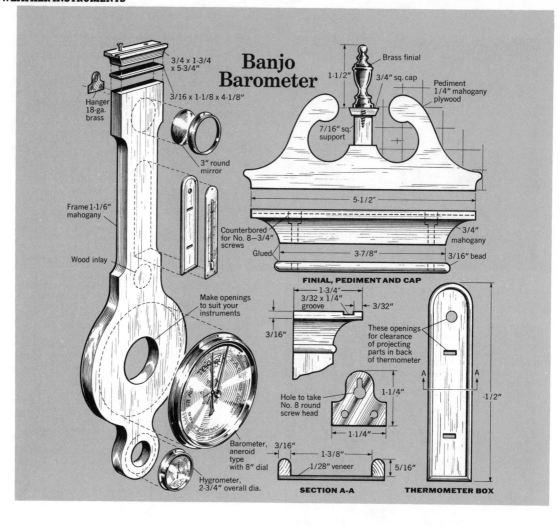

Banjo Barometer

3/4 x 1-3/4 x 5-3/4"

3/16 x 1-1/8 x 4-1/8"

Hanger 18-ga. brass

Frame 1-1/6" mahogany

Wood inlay

3" round mirror

Counterbored for No. 8—3/4" screws

Make openings to suit your instruments

Barometer, aneroid type with 8" dial

Hygrometer, 2-3/4" overall dia.

Brass finial

1-1/2" 3/4" sq. cap

Pediment 1/4" mahogany plywood

7/16" sq. support

5-1/2"

3/4" mahogany

Glued   3-7/8"   3/16" bead

FINIAL, PEDIMENT AND CAP

1-3/4"
3/32 x 1/4" groove
3/32"
3/16"

These openings for clearance of projecting parts in back of thermometer

Hole to take No. 8 round screw head

1-1/4"

1-1/4"

A   A

1/2"

3/16"   1-3/8"
1/28" veneer   5/16"

SECTION A-A   **THERMOMETER BOX**

The finish can be anything you like on mahogany, from natural color to dark reddish brown, the latter being achieved by staining. Use a wiping stain so you can control more closely the depth of color. Then apply paste wood filler, wipe off, following directions on the can, and apply sealer when dry. Follow with at least two coats of semigloss finish. Carefully rub down the last coat with very fine (No. 4-0) steel wool until you have a beautiful satiny gloss.

All the fittings (including the barometer, hygrometer, thermometer and mirror) with matching silvered dials, plus the brass finial, are available in kit form. While an oval "shell" inlay was used in the original barometer, the kit includes a round inlay as shown in the photo at the right.

THE KIT includes all the instruments, mirror, finial and round "shell" inlay.

Inside moves

■ A HEALTHY 6-FOOT MAN exerts 2,000 pounds of force to lift a 200-pound object from the floor to chest level. It may not be a superhuman feat. But physical forces involved in such a move have sent an estimated 250,000 Americans to the doctor every year. Thanks to our early struggle throughout history with moving large objects, we've learned that simple tools—levers, wheels, rollers, inclined planes and pulleys—can make the job survivable, *if* you do it right.

Before you set out to move heavy boxes, appliances or furniture, do warmup exercises. Five minutes of bending and stretching, jumping jacks and situps may make you feel self-conscious. But warming up will prevent about 20 percent of muscle injuries reported in household moves.

Most muscle tears and back pains come from positioning yourself incorrectly before you lift. To pick up a heavy box, for instance, most of us simply bend over, place our hands under the object and heave ho. For better load distribution, squat in front of the box and place your hands under it as far forward as you can reach comfortably. Now the arms are being used as levers and the large thigh muscles are taking a big share of the load.

Moving a large appliance is the next biggest

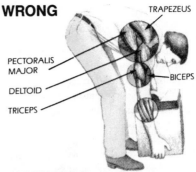

WRONG

TRAPEZEUS

PECTORALIS MAJOR

DELTOID

TRICEPS

BICEPS

MOST MUSCLE tears and back pulls happen when a heavy object is lifted straight up, placing all the strain on the lower back and upper arm muscles (above). By squatting down and picking up the object at the bottom forward end (below), the arm acts as a lever and larger thigh muscles help distribute the load evenly and safely.

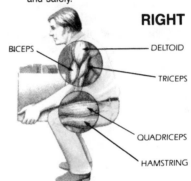

RIGHT

BICEPS

DELTOID

TRICEPS

QUADRICEPS

HAMSTRING

How To Move A Refrigerator/Freezer

TO MOVE ANY LARGE OBJECT without casters, cut a set of rollers from 3-inch dowels or PVC pipes (metal pipes damage floors). Tip object and set one dowel underneath. Push at top and set dowel with your foot.

SLIDE A SHEET OF PLYWOOD underneath the tipped object. The first roller or dowel you inserted will help make way for wood sheet as you push it about two-thirds in. Slip three dowels under the wood sheet.

WITH DOWELS ORIENTED in the direction you want to go, slowly roll the object forward. Just as the rear roller is about to be left behind, you should insert a spare roller under the leading edge of the refrigerator.

cause of muscle injury. The most common mishaps occur with refrigerator moves. If your refrigerator is on casters, all you have to do is pull up rugs along the route of travel or lay down skids in the form of wood boards or linoleum strips. But, if the refrigerator has no casters, you might want to set up a roller system.

You'll need several sections of 3-inch dowels or PVC pipe, and a sheet of plywood the width of the appliance. The rollers should be at least 2 feet long. Tip the appliance and set one dowel underneath so the object you're moving is in a slightly tipped position.

Next, push the plywood board under the appliance about two-thirds of the way. Spread three dowels evenly under the plywood. Go to the other side of the appliance and start pushing gently. As you move, rear dowels will fall out and you'll want to replace them up front.

There also is a range of hand trucks and dollies designed especially for household moves.

The next biggest cause of moving injuries is improper moving of large objects up stairs. You can make the task even more painless with the help of a pulley system, a 2 × 4, a pair of planks and a length of rope.

Whatever the object, remove all hinges, drawers and contents before starting upstairs. Lay the planks on either side of the stairwell up the full length of stairs. Set the 2 × 4 in a doorway at the head of the stairs. It serves as the anchor for your pulley system. If there's no door, you'll have to find a place to fasten a block and tackle or garage ratchet hoist a couple of feet in front of the upper landing. Hook the working end of the lever and pulley system to the object being moved.

Setting up is a one-person job, but moving large objects up stairs is really a job for two. The stronger worker should be at the top of the stairs, pulling the rope. The other mover should stand behind the furniture, slightly bent over and pushing to make sure the object stays on the planks.

Carrying boxes

Carrying boxes over long distances, and especially up stairs, is almost always done the

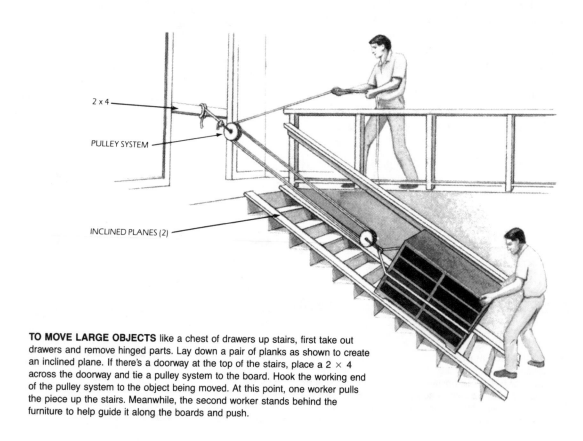

2 x 4

PULLEY SYSTEM

INCLINED PLANES (2)

TO MOVE LARGE OBJECTS like a chest of drawers up stairs, first take out drawers and remove hinged parts. Lay down a pair of planks as shown to create an inclined plane. If there's a doorway at the top of the stairs, place a 2 × 4 across the doorway and tie a pulley system to the board. Hook the working end of the pulley system to the object being moved. At this point, one worker pulls the piece up the stairs. Meanwhile, the second worker stands behind the furniture to help guide it along the boards and push.

Carrying Boxes Over Distances

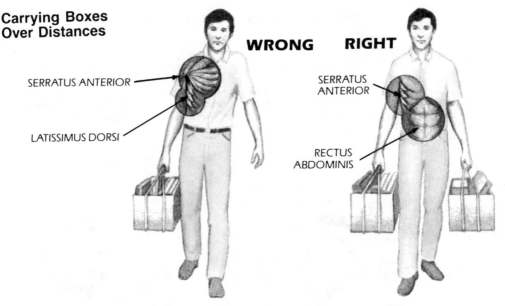

WRONG   **RIGHT**

SERRATUS ANTERIOR

LATISSIMUS DORSI

SERRATUS ANTERIOR

RECTUS ABDOMINIS

THE KEY TO ANY SUCCESSFUL MOVING PROJECT is proper weight distribution. A major cause of injuries is the one-handed method of carrying boxes and other heavy objects. Switching the box from hand to hand strains the latissimus dorsi—a major cause of upper back pain. By carrying two boxes of about the same mass by a handle or rope, the strong rectus abdominis muscles help distribute the weight, taking strain off back.

wrong way, according to medical consultants. Most of us place a handle or rope on the box and pick it up with one hand, shifting hands as we go. This constant shifting causes a heavy strain on the latissimus dorsi muscles, leading to upper back strain.

By packing two (or more) boxes with even weight distribution and tying them with a handle or length of rope at the top, you can set yourself up for a more healthy moving experience. Lifting a box with each arm will distribute the weight across the thick and strong rectus abdominis muscles around the stomach. The even weight distribution might feel like extra weight, but that's more of a state of mind than anything else. The evenly distributed weight will place far less strain on any individual muscle than will the shifted weight of one box.

Moves around the garage

Most moves around the garage are pretty straightforward. But there's one trick that you might find helpful.

If your car dies on the street near your driveway and the conditions are right, you can single-handedly tow it off the street using a floor jack.

Because floor jacks are fitted with swiveling platforms and caster-type rear wheels, the device can be used to dolly a car out of the street. Move carefully, watching for any movement of the jack away from the jack point. If the driveway is walled off, you also have to be very careful not to get sandwiched between the car and a wall.

A car can be moved with a floor jack from the front or the rear, but the front pulling method is best. Set the jack under the centermost part of the jack point and point the jack handle in the direction you want to go. Now, jack up the car just enough to get the tires off the road.

With the brakes off and car in neutral, slowly and carefully pull on the handle. You should not have to bend so low that your head is below your waist, nor should you have to rock back on your heels more than a fraction of an inch. Otherwise, you'll tear at an array of muscles including all the back muscles, the triceps and the latissimus dorsi.

If the car starts rolling so fast it can't be stopped by pushing forward on the jack, lower the jack so the wheels touch the ground again. Moving a car like this should never be performed unless you have a fairly level driveway with arms-length clearance from any walls.

Basic principles of safe moving

Moving heavy objects around the home, shop and garage is something most of us do at least a

Moving A Stalled Car With A Jack

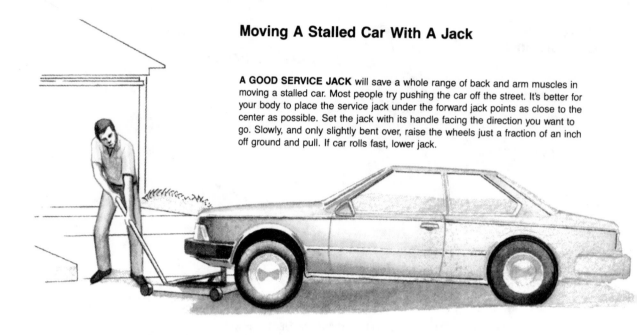

A GOOD SERVICE JACK will save a whole range of back and arm muscles in moving a stalled car. Most people try pushing the car off the street. It's better for your body to place the service jack under the forward jack points as close to the center as possible. Set the jack with its handle facing the direction you want to go. Slowly, and only slightly bent over, raise the wheels just a fraction of an inch off ground and pull. If car rolls fast, lower jack.

couple of times a month. You may not have to perform any of the specific tasks we covered here, but the general principles apply.

● When lifting heavy objects, keep them close to your body. This provides balance and weight distribution.

● Always try to put most of the load on your leg and thigh muscles. They are stronger than any other muscle set and relying on them will take most of the weight off your back.

● Plant your feet close to the object being lifted to ensure greater reliance on leg and thigh muscles.

● Wear a thick, heavy belt (sacroiliac belts are available at most medical aid shops) when lifting.
● Work with rhythm.
● Always warm up before working. Take breaks, since working when fatigued causes muscle damage. Dress comfortably for the work, and protect yourself from drafts.

Finally, set up any moving job with an advance plan. It's best to walk through the move with a tape measure in hand before starting. If you have to stop in the middle, you'll lose the advantage of the warmup and injury may result.

Two Easy-To-Build Moving Aids

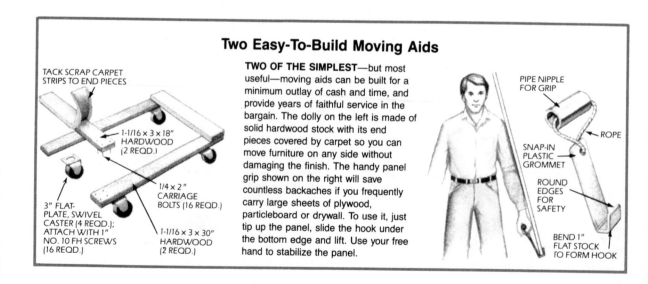

TACK SCRAP CARPET STRIPS TO END PIECES

1-1/16 × 3 × 18" HARDWOOD (2 REQD.)

1/4 × 2" CARRIAGE BOLTS (16 REQD.)

3" FLAT-PLATE, SWIVEL CASTER (4 REQD.); ATTACH WITH 1" NO. 10 FH SCREWS (16 REQD.)

1-1/16 × 3 × 30" HARDWOOD (2 REQD.)

TWO OF THE SIMPLEST—but most useful—moving aids can be built for a minimum outlay of cash and time, and provide years of faithful service in the bargain. The dolly on the left is made of solid hardwood stock with its end pieces covered by carpet so you can move furniture on any side without damaging the finish. The handy panel grip shown on the right will save countless backaches if you frequently carry large sheets of plywood, particleboard or drywall. To use it, just tip up the panel, slide the hook under the bottom edge and lift. Use your free hand to stabilize the panel.

PIPE NIPPLE FOR GRIP

ROPE

SNAP-IN PLASTIC GROMMET

ROUND EDGES FOR SAFETY

BEND 1" FLAT STOCK TO FORM HOOK

Save yourself from drowning!

NEAR JACKSON, MI, an 18-year-old college student driving alone "lost it," went sideways off the road and plunged through the ice of a deep pond. The rolling car eliminated any hope that air might be trapped in the passenger compartment. The youth struggled, took on water and lost consciousness.

Luckily a following driver spotted the accident and alerted the authorities. It was 38 minutes later, however, before rescuers pulled the victim from the water. There was no apparent pulse; no signs of life. He was declared "dead at the scene."

While the body was being loaded into the ambulance, however, the "dead" man gasped. Startled rescuers immediately began revival efforts. At the hospital a team of doctors worked over the boy for two hours. After 13 more hours of respiratory support, the student "woke up." He instantly recognized his mother, who was at his bedside.

Attendant doctors, who had expected brain damage in someone deprived of oxygen for more than four minutes, were even more surprised shortly thereafter when the lad picked up his college career and completed it with A grades.

The apparently unusual case, it turns out, isn't so unusual at all. Today, after several years of scientific investigation prompted and encouraged by the U.S. Coast Guard and the Michigan Sea Grant Program, investigators know that sudden contact of the head and face with "cold" water (anything below 70° F. is classified as "cold" by the Coast Guard) may touch off a primitive response in humans known as the "mammalian diving reflex."

HUNTERS and fishermen falling overboard from boats are prime hypothermia victims. As shown here, waders will float a fisherman who lies still.

HELP position extends survival time.

MARKED AREAS lose body heat.

DON'T gun it while standing aft.

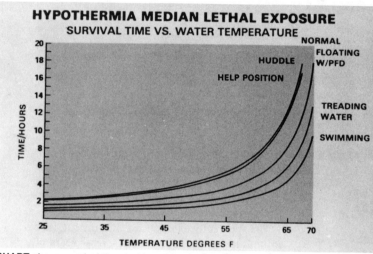

HYPOTHERMIA MEDIAN LETHAL EXPOSURE
SURVIVAL TIME VS. WATER TEMPERATURE

NORMAL
FLOATING
W/PFD
HUDDLE
HELP POSITION
TREADING
WATER
SWIMMING

TIME/HOURS
20 18 16 14 12 10 8 6 4 2

25 35 45 55 65 70
TEMPERATURE DEGREES F

CHART shows survival time lost in cold water by swimming or other exertion.

FOAM BELT pad protects thorax from cold and keeps the head high.

IMPROPERLY WORN life vests lift out of water and lose buoyancy value.

THIS HUNTING jacket PFD insulates body, and floats. Hood warms head.

SKI BELTS are not approved as PFDs. They provide too little buoyancy.

The frigid water triggers complex physiological responses that shut down the blood circulation to most parts of the body except heart, lungs and brain. Though the blood contains only a limited amount of oxygen, it can be enough, investigators have learned, to sustain life and prevent damage to brain tissue for considerable periods of time, once the body's internal temperature has dropped. A cooled-down brain needs less oxygen than one at normal temperature.

This phenomenon has long been known to researchers. It permits deep-diving mammals like whales, porpoises and seals to remain active at frigid depths for long periods.

In humans, unhappily, the phenomenon is not quite that convenient—despite the unique life-extending time it may provide in rare cases.

"Hypothermia," the medical term for dropping the body's internal temperature below its normal 98.6° F., can produce a number of disastrous results. While it may take 10 to 15 minutes before the "core" temperature starts to drop, surface tissues cool quickly. A victim may experience labored breathing and stiffness of limbs and hands.

As core temperature drops to 95° there will be violent shivering; at 90° to 95°, mental facilities cloud; at 86° to 90° there's muscular rigidity and loss of consciousness. Below 86° come diminished respiration and possible heart failure. Below 80°, respiration becomes almost undetectable and death is imminent.

Investigators now believe that something like a third of all the boating drownings reported in one recent year, according to best available estimates, probably were not drownings at all but deaths due to hypothermia. Even more tragic, they suspect that in some 20 to 30 percent of those cases, the victim probably was not dead when found even though there was no discernible pulse, no apparent breathing, eyes were dilated, color was bluish and rigidity had set in—all usual signs of death in familiar warm-water drownings.

Threat to hunters

The state liaison officer for the U.S. Coast Guard's Second District headquarters in St. Louis has been traveling the country spreading a new gospel about these discoveries and what people can and should do about them. He points out that the primary cause of death in autumn hunting accidents is not gunshot wounds, but "drowning," and that many of those so-called drownings are really hypothermia deaths.

"Some victims don't even have water in their lungs," he reveals. "We lose all kinds of them every year. They make a blind out of a 14-foot boat, stand up to shoot, lose their balance and go over the side. Water in many lakes seldom gets above 60°, even in summer. During spring and fall floods it may get down to 40°. Worse, those guys usually are hypothermic to start with from sitting there on a cold morning waiting for the ducks. On top of it, they've been drinking to keep warm. The birds come over, the nimrods stand up, stiff and wobbly, fire, and over they go. The cold water hits them and that's it."

Another favorite gaffe, according to the Coast Guard, is to reach over with one hand, while standing, goose the outboard throttle, and get pitched over the transom when the boat surges ahead.

How do you protect yourself in cold water? For boatmen, the Coast Guard emphasizes "personal flotation devices" (now the preferred term for lifejacket). And you don't just carry them along; you *wear* them. In tests, even experts sometimes take 10 minutes trying to climb into a lifejacket in the water.

The Coast Guard has been running tests on a new family of PFDs, scientifically designed for flotation and warmth in cold water. Doctors have found several body areas extremely vulnerable to the cold—head, sides of thorax and the groin.

Insulation vital

One new PFD is an insulated, hooded hunting jacket with built-in flotation. A strap goes around the crotch so it can't ride up. Other new devices are foam plastic pads laced in place beneath outer garments. Both types will keep a man's head well above water; the hooded jacket protects it from weather.

Though not as insulative, approved life vests are even a help in an emergency. Unfortunately, most people don't know how to put them on properly. In tests, even Coast Guard personnel didn't know kids' from adults' sizes, and one Academy instructor tried to put on an approved vest inside out.

Actually, ordinary woolen clothing will provide flotation if the person in the water doesn't panic and force the air from the fibers. And despite what you may have heard, a fisherman's chest waders will pop his feet up and float him if he doesn't thrash.

Cold water dos and don'ts

DO:

1. **Wear a float coat,** a PFD or several layers of clothing when you're hunting or fishing in a boat. When the water temperature is 50° F., a clothed person can survive an average of three hours in a PFD.
2. **Try to keep lungs filled with air** to maintain buoyancy.
3. **Use minimum movement** to prevent the escape of trapped air in your clothing. An average person who is treading water or swimming in a PFD will lose body heat about 35 percent faster than he would when holding still.

4. Take advantage of floating objects, such as boats, paddles and so forth for added buoyancy.
5. Maintain HELP (Heat Escape Lessening Posture—see diagram) until help arrives. If two or more people are in the water, huddle.

DO NOT:
1. Panic. Most victims are conscious when they enter the water; most drownings happen only 10 feet away from safety; action taken in the first 10 seconds can mean survival or death.
2. Struggle. You'll squeeze out air trapped in your clothing. Ingesting cold water may constrict the breathing passages and induce "dry drowning."
3. Swim for land that's over a mile away.
4. Remove clothing.
5. Use so-called "drownproofing" techniques in water that's colder than 72° F.

What about drownproofing?

The principles of a procedure known as drownproofing undoubtedly have saved many lives in shallow, sun-warmed lakes and pools where water temperature climbs above 72° F. in summertime. The technique involves floating almost motionlessly for long periods, relying on the natural buoyancy of the body and its tendency to hang in a semi-vertical position in water, head just breaking the surface. Potential drowning victims tend to thrash around in futile efforts to "climb on top" of the water, but the drownproofing concept teaches them to stay alive through maximum conservation of energy.

Instruction in the technique usually begins at poolside, practicing the correct position—head forward, arms down, legs together. With a friend to help at the pool's shallow end (left), the student kneels on the bottom and tilts head back to bring nose and mouth above surface to inhale fresh air, then tilts head forward to exhale. Final step (center) finds student hanging suspended (arms and legs positioned as in the right photo) in deep water by herself—nose and mouth above the surface where they can take air as needed—without need for exertion. At that point, the student has been "drownproofed."

In water below 72° F., however, forget drownproofing, says the U.S. Coast Guard—unless you're caught with only bathing attire and no flotation gear. In cold water, the greatest body heat loss is from the head and neck. Since drownproofing requires immersion of those areas, the onset of hypothermia, followed by death, can be brought about with distressing swiftness.

If you are unfortunate enough to go overboard without attire containing some insulative or buoyant potential, then drownproofing, treading water or swimming may be your only chance.

Boating emergencies

■ THE FIRST LAW of boating safety would probably be: "Do everything you can to avoid an emergency." Know your boat and operate it properly; carry all the right safety equipment and know how to use it; keep your boat, motor and gear in top shape.

But when you *are* faced with an emergency (and it happens to the best of us), the first thing to remember is *don't panic*. Things are seldom as bad as they seem, and for every emergency there's a simple drill. Check the following pages for some important "what-to-do-if" rules.

Your boat suddenly capsizes . . .

Count heads immediately. If anyone is missing, check behind or under the boat. Don life preservers or grab floating cushions. Gather everybody around the boat and make them stay there. (Swimming for shore is risky. It's always farther than it looks.) To right the boat, push down on one side to impart a rollover motion. Be careful: Don't get hit.

Round-chine boats can be cleared of considerable amounts of water by rocking them from side to side. Spilled passengers grip opposite gunnels, and those on one side bear down while those on the opposite side let the boat rise so that water spills out over the low side. A few such rolls will remove enough water to allow one man to scramble aboard (over the transom) and finish bailing from the inside.

Righting a small sailboat is easier than righting a runabout. Just place your feet on the centerboard, grip the gunnel with both hands and pull the boat right side up. But if your boat has an aluminum mast that isn't completely sealed at the ends, slip a buoyant cushion under the tip as soon as possible after going over. This will keep the mast from sinking and turning the boat completely upside down, which will make it considerably harder to right. While you're still in the water, empty the hull as much as you can by splashing or bailing. Then reboard over the transom to avoid capsizing (unless you happen to be an old hand at it).

Once righted, you can bail out the hull, provided the gunnel is even slightly above water. If the transom cutout is submerged, have passengers bear down on the bow while someone bails the well. Use anything handy for bailing—drinking cups, tin cans, hand splashing or even the bilge pump if it wasn't lost during capsizing. After you've made a little progress, boost the lightest man aboard to bail from the inside. It's slow, but it works.

A water-filled sailboat may flop over again when you're bailing. To help prevent this (and to make the boat easier to right), the sails should be dropped and the centerboard lowered completely before you haul the boat right side up. With some hulls, it's possible to turn the boom into a stabilizing outrigger by lashing it to a cleat at right angles to the boat and placing a buoyant cushion under the end. The important thing to remember in any capsizing is not to exhaust yourself trying to do the impossible. If you can't right the hull easily, hold on and wait for rescue.

You've hit something and holed the hull . . .

If the hole is forward on a planing hull, it may be possible to keep it above water while running for shore simply by maintaining planing speed. In choppy water, it's a good idea to have somebody crawl up under the foredeck and stuff a rag into the hole or block the opening by pressing a handful of rags over it. Just hold a steady planing speed and avoid sharp turns.

A hole in the cockpit that can be reached from the inside should be plugged with rags or articles of clothing, which can be held in place by having a passenger stand on them. (For that matter, boats have made shore from miles away with a small hole plugged by somebody simply pressing a foot over it.) If the boat has a self-bailer, use it. Have the passengers bail, or man the bilge pump. The boat's speed will depend on the location of the hole. Start slow and check the flow as you increase speed. Aim for the least amount of leakage.

An emergency patch for a hole in the cockpit can sometimes be made by wedging gear under a seat to hold the preserver cushion against the leak.

A hole near the chine can sometimes be lifted above the water by shifting passengers and gear to heel the boat. Even if the hole doesn't rise above the waterline, the flow will be reduced by bringing it nearer the surface. As with any hole, block the flow by stuffing the hole with whatever you happen to have at hand—sweaters, jackets, bathing suits or other articles of clothing. Then head for shore at low speed, keeping the hole side up on turns and swinging wide to avoid taking on additional water.

A hole under the floorboards that is inaccessible from the cockpit must be plugged from the outside, though shifting weight may also be of some help. Assuming the water is calm and you're a good swimmer, shut off the motor and go over the side. You'll probably have to locate the hole by feel. If it's small, stuff a rag into it. Use a cushion or a pad or rags as a patch for larger holes, holding it snug against the leak by drawing a rope tight around the hull. Then start bailing and make for shore. If possible, head for the nearest beach, since a badly holed boat may sink at dockside before it can be hauled out, especially during off-hours.

If you can't make it to shore and you're in a boat that can sink completely (such as a sailboat with a heavy keel), get as close to land as you can before going over the side in life preservers. Before you abandon ship, trail a long line astern with a float tied to the end; a plastic oil container might be a likely choice here. This float will serve as a marker for salvage operations. If you have time, also take a "fix" on land objects to help locate the boat.

You've run aground on a bar...

Kill the motor immediately and check for hull damage, fuel-line leaks or spilled fuel, especially if the impact was hard. Then tilt up the lower unit or stern drive and make sure the cooling intakes aren't fouled. Before trying to push off, pump out the bilge to lighten the boat, and move passengers aft (assuming you've grounded at the bow). Use a paddle, boat hook or water ski to pole off, facing to the side or aft to avoid falling overboard.

If you're grounded at the stern, use a pole or anything else handy to pry the bow around so you're headed in the opposite direction. Remember that the best way off is almost always the way you came on, since your hull has already plowed the channel. No matter where you're grounded, chances are it rises still higher ahead of you. Use a rag pad over the gunnel to avoid marring it when prying. When headed in the right direction, use the same kind of prying action at the transom to walk the boat toward open water. If you have passengers, of course, move them up to the bow to take weight off the stern while prying.

If you can't pole off, leave one person aboard who knows how to handle the boat and have everyone else who can swim go over the side. This can lighten the boat by as much as a quarter of a ton. To get free, squat with your back against the bow, then push up and back as you straighten your legs. (*Don't* try it in a mucky bottom.) When the boat is free, swim to it.

If the bottom is soft, shift passengers to one side to tilt the boat. This raises the deepest point of the hull (especially one with a deep-V) and may free the boat enough so you can pole back to deep water. When free, hand-crank the motor with the switch off and listen for sounds of internal damage that might be worsened by electric starting. If all sounds right, start the motor and check the cooling outlet to make sure the system is working right. If you lost a prop blade and don't have a spare prop aboard, run for shore at the lowest rpm that provides headway.

If you're alone and grounded on a mucky bottom, there's a good chance you can work the boat free by rocking it from side to side. The safest way to do this is to stand in the cockpit with your feet spread wide apart and rhythmically shift your weight from one foot to the other until you feel the boat begin to rock. Once you've got it rocking, throw your weight into the rhythm to make it rock harder. If you're grounded at the bow and have to rock from the foredeck, tie a lifeline around your waist. When the hull breaks free, pole off.

Be a savvy RV pilot

TRAILER CARGO on a flatbed trailer must be secured as well. Without chain binders at all four corners, the racer could plunge forward during an emergency stop, and crash through the camper.

■ ALL IT TAKES is one close call or an accident to make you realize that there are some special tricks to driving a recreational vehicle or pulling a trailer. It is important to make sure that everything is securely fastened and you are driving with confidence but defensively.

While under way in any kind of recreational vehicle, make a habit of stowing away securely all loose gear in your camper. Heavy tools should be stored in a special bin, not in the cab or passenger compartment. Passengers should remain seated and preferably safety belted.

Pickup camper owners should pay more attention to tie-downs. A strong wind can blow the camper out of the cargo box. Vibration can loosen turnbuckles, so they should be regularly tightened. A camper body that pulls out during an accident may then be struck by a following car.

Travel trailer accidents can result when a big trailer towed by too small a car starts to sway. Other causes include too much speed and cheap bumper hitches. Use equalizing hitches and anti-sway bars.

Motor homes should allow extra stopping distance, avoid tailgating and save brakes by using lower gears.

Tires must be the right size and with good tread of the same pattern at each end of an axle. Slow down during heavy rains.

Strap down boats carried on camper tops, bicycles and trail bikes on bumpers.

Should an accident happen, make sure all passengers are out of the RV, shut off the motor and propane supply, take pictures, record witnesses and light warning flares away from possible fumes.

MIRRORS at the left and right are particularly needed by the RV driver as faster cars continually pass him. Use a windshield scraper when mud and snow collect if the mirror is too far out for easy cleaning.

STABILIZER JACKS should be checked regularly. If your tent-trailer jacks are left in a down position by mistake, they could catch in a chuckhole or on railroad tracks and tear the trailer away from the car.

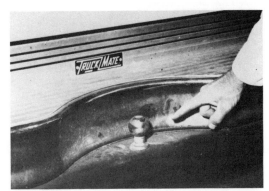

BUMPERS of most cars and trucks will flex too much and are not usually designed to take the many stresses of towing unless they are specially braced as shown here. Stiffeners should run back to the frame rails if you are towing large trailers.

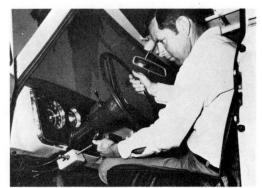

ELECTRIC BRAKES for the trailer you are towing should be adjusted on a regular schedule before there is any chance of an emergency stop. Set them so that they come on just ahead of the car brakes to prevent any possibility the trailer might jacknife.

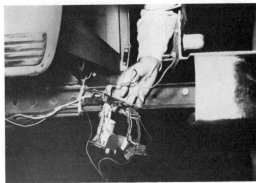

THIS ELECTRICIAN'S nightmare of wires is typical of using too many trailer hookups. This might happen if you use boat, horse and travel trailers interchangeably. In this situation the couplers could drag on the pavement and cause a fire. Keep all connections neat.

THIS PICKUP camper hit a carport roof and crumpled the corner of the cab. Fortunately it did not twist or buckle the frame. The accident revealed the basic strength of this somewhat fragile-looking rig. The window glass didn't even break.

ROLLED OVER three times, this camper body shows surprising strength. It is made with foam-sandwich construction. Although the truck landed up-side down, only the cab was badly damaged after skidding off the road on a rainy day.

FRONT-BUMPER load, like the trail-bike shown in this photo, can cause a serious accident if it falls in front of RV. For safety's sake, a rear bumper mounting is much better. But be sure the unit is set in a special carrying rack and double-strapped as well.

A TOWED VEHICLE should be given special care in hooking up. Use a strong safety chain plus proper brake and light couplers. The hitch should be strong enough so that it can take the strains of a heavy load. The extension bumper shown in this photo had too much flex.

EXTRA-WIDE RIMS must be used when you switch to superwide tires. Without this precaution you are inviting an accident. The rim shown fits 10-16.5 Super-Single that provides the truck with the wheel strength to match the tire weight capacity.

BUILT-IN jack legs must be hinged and strapped securely in place to prevent dropping and dragging the camper off the truck body while it is in motion. Sidewall brackets, floor bolts and turnbuckles can all be combined to hold the camper in the truck box.

SHUT OFF the propane tanks before starting a trip as a safety precaution. This simple step could help prevent a fire in the event of an accident in which the LP gas lines are ruptured. Prechill your LP refrigerator and start it again at the campground.

TURNBUCKLE hold-downs have a way of vibrating loose, especially on a rough road. Check them at every gas stop. Don't try to tighten them by applying leverage with a long-handled tool as it might break them. Snug turnbuckles tight with your hand.

REAR LIGHT check is important in daytime as well as at night. It is one of many safety checks you should make before any trip. Be sure to examine your brake stoplights and turn indicators regularly and always carry spare bulbs for them.

Safe cycling secrets

■ WHAT DO YOU DO when that summer thunderstorm hits—stop your motorcycle or keep going? With a little common sense, you can keep right on going and arrive safely at your destination. That is, if you know a few basics about slick-surface cycling.

One of the basics of successful motorcycle riding is to feel relaxed with it. You must imagine that two-wheeler as a natural extension of your mind and body. Because the bike is so responsive to your slightest movements, you must be careful not to *overcontrol* it on a slippery surface.

But before you can feel relaxed with that two-wheeler, you must first have the right frame of mind. You must believe that you're capable of riding safely on slick surfaces.

If you have a strong fear of spilling, your negative attitude will affect your riding. Remember: Don't fear wet roads; respect them.

What to wear

A good helmet and rainsuit are necessary, along with effective eye protection. For maximum eye and facial protection, a face shield is ideal. It not only protects the eyes, but it also saves your face from the stinging impact of raindrops.

Snug-fitting, large-lens goggles offer good eye protection, but they don't provide the facial coverage of a face shield. Whether you use goggles or a shield, get the Hydron-treated plastic as it absorbs moisture and minimizes "fogging-up."

Waterproof gloves are necessary, if you want to keep your hands from slipping off the grips and controls.

WATCH ROAD SURFACES

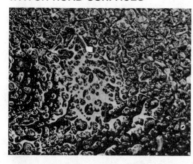

KEEP YOUR EYE on the road surface: At left is an asphalt surface; it's slippery, but tires get some bite on the high spots. Center is a classic hazard of wet leaves on a turn. On the right is a combination of slippery surfaces: leaves on shiny, smooth crosswalk markings, and loose pieces of broken pavement that increase the danger.

WATCH ROAD HAZARDS

ROAD HAZARDS are many and varied, but three of the most dangerous are shown above. Railroad tracks shown at left should be crossed at right angles; watch for washouts alongside the tracks. Gratings (center) come in all shapes and sizes and are slippery when wet. Also watch out for expansion joints (right) such as on bridges.

CHECK TIRE PRESSURE

TIRE air pressure is critical. It is better to be underinflated than overinflated, but the best situation is to check the p.s.i. at every gas fill-up and see that it is as specified.

CHECK CHAIN TENSION

PROPER CHAIN tension is important for insuring that power delivery to the rear tire's contact patch is smooth and positive. There should always be ¾-inch play midway between the sprockets. See the text.

KNOW ABOUT HYDROPLANING

WHEN YOUR TIRES lift off the pavement and ride on a thin layer of water, you're hydroplaning. The speed at which this occurs depends on many variables (see text). Since control is lost when this happens, be prepared for the phenomenon especially if there's enough water on the road for raindrops to dimple.

SELECT RIGHT TIRES

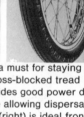

RIGHT TIRES are a must for staying on two wheels. Cross-blocked tread (above, right) provides good power delivery to road while allowing dispersal of water. Ribbed tire (right) is ideal front tire. It minimizes sideslip.

Top off your wet-weather gear with a pair of nonslip-soled, lightweight boots.

Prepping your bike

Besides getting yourself prepped for slick-surface cycling, you've got to make sure your bike is ready, too.

Tire condition is extremely important, so let's start with tires.

If you do much road riding, you should have suitable tread designs. The two basic road-tread designs are the ribbed and the universal. The ribbed design is good for up front because its circumferential-rib construction resists sideslipping when the bike is banked. This tire design wears well and provides good steering. Its lack of cross-block tread, however, makes it unsuitable for the rear, as it'll spin rather easily under power.

The universal design, on the other hand, can be used on both front and rear. This tire features a closely spaced tread-block pattern, which makes it effective for delivering the engine's power to the ground.

A variation of the universal design is the trials-universal tread pattern. Its tread blocks are more widely spaced than those on the universal; therefore, it doesn't provide as good a "bite" on a slippery surface as does the universal.

The sports knobby has even less rubber to contact the road than the trials-universal design. If you must ride on a wet surface with the knobby type, use extreme caution. This tire is meant for dirt riding *only*.

The rear chain must be lubricated and tensioned properly to insure smooth delivery of power to the rear tire's contact patch.

A dry chain will bind and jerk around the sprockets. If it's too loose, it'll surge or whip as it travels between the sprockets. A primary-drive chain (if your bike has one) is even less tolerant of lack of lubrication and improper adjustment when it comes to delivering the engine's power smoothly.

Check the sprockets, too. If their teeth are pointed, hook-shaped, or—worse yet—worn to nubs, replace them. Worn sprockets will make a worn chain alternately tighten and loosen at certain points of its travel.

Don't run a worn chain with new sprockets; by the same token, don't put a new chain on worn sprockets.

Don't overlook the throttle, clutch, and brake cables either. They need adequate lubrication so that they won't bind anywhere. Make sure the throttle-cable housing doesn't bend sharply anywhere and restrict the movement of the cable inside.

Also check for throttle-cable binding as you move the handlebar from side to side.

Check the brakes to see that they don't grab or drag. They should take hold without requiring heavy applications of pressure. It's important, too, that the clutch engage and disengage smoothly. Furthermore, you'll need to keep that engine tuned. When you twist that throttle, you want the engine to respond at that instant—not a moment later when the rear tire is on some slippery substance.

Surface conditions

Although there are only two basic kinds of paved road—asphalt and concrete—there are infinite variations of them regarding surface conditions.

For that reason, you must be on your toes constantly, scanning the road ahead for anything that can make the tires lose adhesion with the road. An otherwise tractional surface can be made slippery by the presence of oil deposits, sand, leaves or other debris. And, especially at night, you may not notice these substances lying on the road.

Now if you've had little or no experience on wet roads, you might want to conduct an "eyeball" inspection of different surfaces some time. That is, squat down and really look a wet surface over. Feel it with your hand. Look for any substance that could enhance the slipperiness of the road surface.

New asphalt generally has a coarser surface texture than concrete. So, even with residual water lying on the road, the tires can still get some adhesion. There are exceptions, however, as some asphalt sections may be worn smooth. Also, beware of worn asphalt roads that have smooth, tarred areas. They can be very slippery when wet.

Furthermore, in hot weather, those tarred spots will be soft and unstable, adding to their slipperiness. They may even have sand sprinkled on them.

The camber of a road must be considered, too. If it has little or no camber, deposits of water will be trapped on the surface.

Regardless of the type of road you ride on, never ride in the middle area of the lane, especially on uphill approaches.

Why?

The center area of a lane is the final resting

place for oil drippings from other vehicles. You'll find heavier deposits of oil on those long uphill lanes frequented by truck traffic. Watch out for concentrations of oil drippings at traffic lights and stop signs, too.

Whenever possible, ride to either side of the lane's center. Riding to one side of the lane has another advantage when it's raining: By staying in the "tire wipe" areas of the vehicle in front of your bike, you can take advantage of the squee-gee effect of that vehicle's tires.

If there's any time that you should be particularly cautious of a wet road, it's during the first few minutes of rainfall that follows a long dry spell.

Those first drops of rain mix with all sorts of oil, dirt, tire-wear particles and other debris to form a slimy mixture that coats the surface. You can t really see it, because it's not very thick. But it's extremely slippery.

Road hazards

What makes slick-surface motorcycling so challenging is the variety of surfaces you encounter. You've read about the need to be on the lookout for oil deposits, leaves, sand and other debris that can enhance the slipperiness of an already slick surface. But what about bridge-floor gratings and expansion joints, manhole covers, crosswalk markings and railroad crossings?

Take railroad crossings: Ever since the first motorcycle sputtered down the road, they have been responsible for cyclists parting company with their bikes. Even when they're dry, rails can be slippery; but when they become wet, they can send a two-wheeler slithering in an instant.

Just remember to approach them at a right angle. Go easy on the gas and stay off the clutch and brakes when traveling over them. Do your braking and down-shifting before you get to them.

And watch it around gas stations. Cars that have just had their tanks filled may slosh gas onto the road as they exit from a station. Gasoline is slipperier than water and it is also virtually unnoticeable on a wet surface.

Hydroplaning

Skidding is a constant threat on wet surfaces, if you don't know what you're doing. But there's another phenomenon that can create moments of panic: hydroplaning. It occurs when a layer of water actually wedges itself between the road and one of the tires, most often the front tire.

Whether hydroplaning occurs or not depends mostly on the speed of the motorcycle and on the amount of water on the road. With modern motorcycles, it's not hard to cruise at speeds higher than 50 mph on wet surfaces.

Because hydroplaning can occur at speeds as low as 35 mph, providing there's enough water on the surface, your bike can turn into a motorized surfboard. Here's a rule of thumb for figuring if there's enough water present to induce hydroplaning. If there's enough water lying on the road for raindrops to make a dimpling effect, there's enough water for hydroplaning. *Watch it!*

Riding technique

Other factors that enter into hydroplaning are the width and tread design of the tires. A worn, wide tire will plane at a lower speed than a narrow tire with a deep-tread design. In addition, the lighter the combined weight of bike and rider, the lower the speed at which hydroplaning will occur.

When it comes to stopping your bike on a wet surface, you must develop a touch of finesse with the brakes. Learn how to decelerate by using the brakes and engine compression together. You can apply the rear brake an instant before the front brake to help stabilize the machine.

If you apply *only* the rear brake, you run the risk of locking it up. It takes more pressure to slow the machine with just one brake. With both brakes, you're distributing braking pressures between them, in smaller amounts. And by downshifting, you employ the services of a third brake: engine compression.

Taking advantage of the retarding effect of engine compression lets you apply less pressure to the brakes than you normally would without downshifting. What's more, a four-stroker will provide more retarding effect than a two-stroker. Take that fact into consideration when you switch from one type of engine to the other.

Once you master slick-surface motorcycling, you'll never have to worry about getting caught in the rain miles from home and having to pull over until the rain stops and the roads dry.

SHOP GUIDE

CUSTOMARY TO METRIC (CONVERSION)
Conversion factors can be carried so far they become impractical. In cases below where an entry is exact it is followed by an asterisk (*). Where considerable rounding off has taken place, the entry is followed by a + or a − sign.

Linear Measure

inches	millimeters
1/16	1.5875*
1/8	3.2
3/16	4.8
1/4	6.35*
5/16	7.9
3/8	9.5
7/16	11.1
1/2	12.7*
9/16	14.3
5/8	15.9
11/16	17.5
3/4	19.05*
13/16	20.6
7/8	22.2
15/16	23.8
1	25.4*

inches	centimeters
1	2.54*
2	5.1
3	7.6
4	10.2
5	12.7*
6	15.2
7	17.8
8	20.3
9	22.9
10	25.4*
11	27.9
12	30.5

feet	centimeters	meters
1	30.48*	.3048*
2	61	.61
3	91	.91
4	122	1.22
5	152	1.52
6	183	1.83
7	213	2.13
8	244	2.44
9	274	2.74
10	305	3.05
50	1524*	15.24*
100	3048*	30.48*

1 yard = .9144* meters
1 rod = 5.0292* meters
1 mile = 1.6 kilometers
1 nautical mile = 1.852* kilometers

Weights

ounces	grams
1	28.3
2	56.7
3	85
4	113
5	142
6	170
7	198
8	227
9	255
10	283
11	312
12	340
13	369
14	397
15	425
16	454

Formula (exact):
ounces × 28.349 523 125* = grams

pounds	kilograms
1	.45
2	.9
3	1.4
4	1.8
5	2.3
6	2.7
7	3.2
8	3.6
9	4.1
10	4.5

1 short ton (2000 lbs) = 907 kilograms (kg)
Formula (exact):
pounds × .453 592 37* = kilograms

Fluid Measure

(Milliliters [ml] and cubic centimeters [cc] are equivalent, but it is customary to use milliliters for liquids.)

1 cu in	=	16.39 ml
1 fl oz	=	29.6 ml
1 cup	=	237 ml
1 pint	=	473 ml
1 quart	=	946 ml
	=	.946 liters
1 gallon	=	3785 ml
	=	3.785 liters

Formula (exact):
fluid ounces × 29.573 529 562 5*
= milliliters

Volume

1 cu in	=	16.39 cubic centimeters (cc)
1 cu ft	=	28 316.7 cc
1 bushel	=	35 239.1 cc
1 peck	=	8 809.8 cc

Area

1 sq in	=	6.45 sq cm
1 sq ft	=	929 sq cm
	=	.093 sq meters
1 sq yd	=	.84 sq meters
1 acre	=	4 046.9 sq meters
	=	.404 7 hectares
1 sq mile	=	2 589 988 sq meters
	=	259 hectares
	=	2.589 9 sq kilometers

Miscellaneous

1 British thermal unit (Btu) (mean) = 1 055.9 joules
1 horsepower = 745.7 watts
= .75 kilowatts
caliber (diameter of a firearm's bore in hundredths of an inch) = .254 millimeters (mm)

1 atmosphere pressure = 101 325* pascals (newtons per sq meter)
1 pound per square inch (psi) = 6 895 pascals
1 pound per square foot = 47.9 pascals
1 knot = 1.85 kilometers per hour
1 mile per hour = 1.6093 kilometers per hour